Choosing and Using ECL

Choosing and Using ECL

Paul L Matthews

GRANADA
London Toronto Sydney New York

Granada Publishing Limited — Technical Books Division
Frogmore, St Albans, Herts AL2 2NF
and
36 Golden Square, London W1R 4AH
515 Madison Avenue, New York, NY 10022, USA
117 York Street, Sydney, NSW 2000, Australia
60 International Boulevard, Rexdale, Ontario R9W 6J2, Canada
61 Beach Road, Auckland, New Zealand

ISBN 0 246 11877 6

First published in Great Britain 1983 by Granada Publishing

Printed in Great Britain by Mackays of Chatham Ltd.

Granada ®
Granada Publishing ®

Contents

Preface

Emitter coupled logic has always been considered as a rather specialised area of semiconductor electronics. Often regarded as a design technique reserved for applications for which the ultimate in high speed was required, it became associated with high power consumption, limited flexibility and difficulty of use. In recent years the emergence of low cost memories and microprocessors has tended to divert attention towards MOS technology instead.

I have been following the progress of ECL developments for several years and find that ECL is not only alive and well – it also represents a very significant force in the communications, instrumentation and aerospace industries. In this book I have tried to follow the development of ECL from the early computer days, through the various logic families to the groups of products which find application on a 'stand alone' basis. These are products such as voltage comparators and frequency dividers which were first introduced as part of a logic family. I have looked at products in each of these groups and offered suggestions to help in their choice and application. Recent product introductions indicate that improvements in bipolar processing will allow circuits of much greater complexity to be manufactured. I have included a chapter on the subject of signal processing as an example of this. Semi-custom ECL and a number of other opportunities for the future have also been included.

Perhaps the most difficult decision I had to take was how to cater for the reader's technical background. ECL products are used in so many specialised areas, by engineers with backgrounds in, say, microwaves rather than logic design. I have tried to avoid unnecessary technical explanations but most readers may find at least one page of this nature. I apologise for this; I asked five different people for advice on what to include and I received five different answers!

I am grateful to a number of people who have taken time to help me produce this book. My wife and daughter have been very patient while I have either been deep in thought or busy typing. Without the support of everyone involved it would have been much more difficult.

Acknowledgements

The author wishes to thank the following for permission to reproduce the Figures listed:
Motorola Semiconductors Ltd., Figs: 2.3, 2.4, 2.12, 2.13, 2.14, 2.16, all Figures in Chapter 3, 4.2, 4.3, 4.4, 4.5, 4.6, 4.7, 4.8, 4.9, 4.11, 4.15, 4.16, 4.17, 6.16, 6.17, 8.14, 8.15, 8.17, 8.18, 8.19, 8.20.
Plessey Semiconductors Ltd., Figs: 1.9, 2.2, 2.8, 2.9, 2.10, 2.15, 5.2, 5.5, 5.9, 5.14, 5.15, 5.16, 5.19, 5.20, 5.21, 5.22, 6.4, 6.10, 6.12, 6.13, 6.15, 6.18, 6.19, 6.20, 6.21, 7.2, 7.4, 7.5, 7.7, 7.8, 7.9, 7.15, 7.18, 8.16, 9.1, 9.2, 10.7.

CHAPTER 1
The birth of emitter coupled logic

Looking back over twenty-five years of emitter coupled logic is a fascinating task. Technology has evolved dramatically — from germanium alloyed junction transistors through silicon planar transistors to the complex integrated circuits of today. Restrictions of low gain, leakage currents and other device limitations are largely irrelevant now, but there still remains one fundamental problem associated with the use of the transistor as a switch. The problem, that of charge storage, was first described by Ebers and Moll* in 1954.

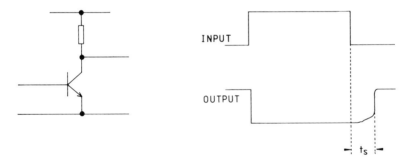

Fig. 1.1 Saturated transistor switch (showing storage time delay)

In the early days of transistor circuit design it was soon realised that saturated switching logic had many advantages — simplicity, low power dissipation and well defined logic voltage levels which gave a good noise margin. To achieve these it was important to drive the transistor fully ON, normally with a base current of one tenth of the collector current. Then it became apparent that the harder and longer a transistor is driven ON, the longer it takes before the excess drive charge (stored in the base or even the

*J. Ebers and J. Moll (1954), 'Large signal behaviour of junction transistors'. *Proc. IRE* **42**, 1761-1772.

collector region of the transistor) flows away and the transistor begins to turn OFF. This storage time delay is shown diagrammatically in fig. 1.1.

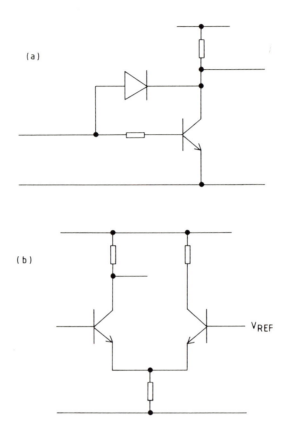

Fig. 1.2 Two methods to reduce storage time (a) Limit saturation
(b) Avoid saturation

During the middle and late 'fifties a number of circuit techniques were described to alleviate the charge storage problem. 'Speed-up' capacitors (across a series base resistor) brought problems of their own; diode-collector clamps had to be carefully toleranced to avoid incorrect operation. But two techniques emerged then as clear leaders and now, twenty-five years later, each has evolved as a major integrated circuit (IC) logic family. The techniques are shown in fig. 1.2.

The circuit of fig. 1.2 (a) retains the advantages of saturated logic levels. When the transistor is OFF the output voltage approaches the supply voltage. As it is turned ON the voltage falls until the clamp diode begins to conduct — at which point the base drive is diverted and saturation is avoided (almost). Nowadays 'Schottky clamped' collector-base junctions perform this function.

The second circuit avoids the saturation problem completely by operating the switching transistor under ideal conditions from a constant current source. The disadvantage is that the voltage levels of 0 and 1 are not widely separated and they drift with temperature. The technique could be considered to switch currents rather than voltages and for that reason was often known as CML (current mode logic), but today it is known as ECL (emitter coupled logic). Circuits of this type were first described by Yourke* in 1957.

A comparison between the developments of these two technologies leads us to look at the 74S Schottky TTL family and the ECL10 000 series. Both offer propagation delays of 3 ns and clock rates of up to 125 MHz. Fig. 1.3 compares the circuit diagrams of simple gates and fig. 1.4 examines the performance characteristics.

A rapid comparison shows that the circuits are of similar complexity and performance, but differ dramatically in logic levels. Whichever is used in a particular application depends on many factors which cannot be considered here, but 74S is a better choice when only a 5 V supply is available and interfacing with TTL or CMOS is important. ECL is generally easier to use provided that certain rules are followed, but it is seldom worth while to use a small number of ECL10K circuits in a predominantly TTL or CMOS system. Despite popular opinion it is often the case that ECL circuitry consumes less power, especially at high speeds (see fig. 1.5).

History of ECL

At the time the first ECL logic families were being introduced there was no clearly defined large market for the products. It was obvious that there would be relatively few industrial applications and manufacturers concentrated on the manufacture of products with the best high speed performance. Motorola introduced their MC300/350 series in 1963 with a propagation delay of 8 ns and toggle rate of 30 MHz. Within four years this had been improved to 4 ns and 70 MHz (ECL2) and subsequently 180 MHz (see figs 1.6 and 1.7). Although both ECL1 (300/350 series) and ECL2

*H.S. Yourke (1957), 'Millimicrosecond transistor current switching circuits', *IRE Trans. Circuit Theory* **CT-4**, 236-240.

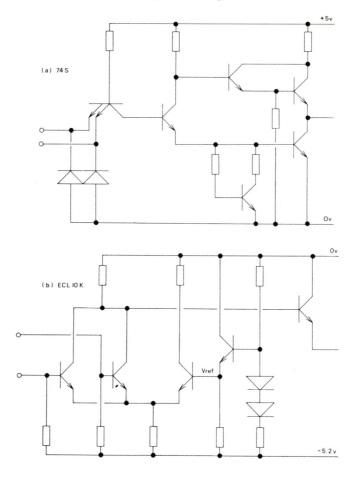

Fig. 1.3 74S and ECL10K gate circuits (a) 74 Schottky (2 input NAND)
(b) ECL10K (2 input NOR)

Fig. 1.4 Relative performance of 74S and ECL10K gates

	74S	ECL10K
Supply voltage	+5.0 V	−5.2 V
Supply current (DC)	4 mA	8 mA*
Supply current (100 MHz)	10 mA	8 mA*
Input voltage (high)	>2 V	>−1.11 V
(low)	<0.8 V	<−1.48 V
Output voltage (high)	>2.7 V	>−0.96 V
(low)	<0.5 V	<−1.65 V

*Depends on output load resistor value

(1000/1200 series) have been discontinued, they paved the way for the introduction of a number of rather different ECL products.

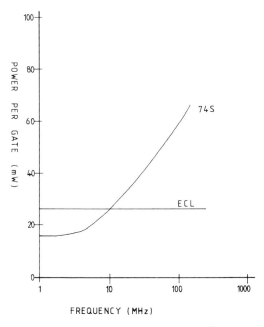

Fig. 1.5 Relative power consumption of ECL and 74S

The principal markets for ECL products at this time were in the computing (central processing and a few peripherals), instrumentation (counters, dividers and similar functions) and communications (counters, dividers for frequency measurement) areas, both commercial and military. In each of these areas the demand for high-speed products was limited to a certain extent by the support circuits – high-frequency amplifiers, oscillators and voltage comparators for example – and at that time such circuits were not widely available.

The more inventive customers realised that since emitter coupled logic is constructed from a series of differential amplifiers and emitter followers then it must be possible to use these for other functions. The MC/SP 1035 line receiver, for example, was quickly adapted as a 100 MHz wideband amplifier by the addition of two external capacitors (fig. 1.8). Each stage has a voltage gain of about five times and as far as I know there were few problems because the circuit was so simple. Sense amplifiers and comparators are also simple to construct using similar techniques. Clock oscillators are more difficult, but normally a single gate

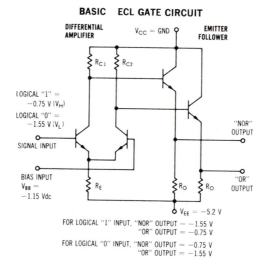

BASIC ECL GATE CIRCUIT

FOR LOGICAL "1" INPUT, "NOR" OUTPUT = −1.55 V
"OR" OUTPUT = −0.75 V
FOR LOGICAL "0" INPUT, "NOR" OUTPUT = −0.75 V
"OR" OUTPUT = −1.55 V

MC300 Series (−55° to +125°C)
MC350 Series (0° to +75°C)

FUNCTIONS AND CHARACTERISTICS ($V_{CC} = 0$, $V_{EE} = -5.2$ V, $T_A = 25°C$)

Function	Type ①		Loading Factor Each Output	Propagation Delay ns typ
	−55 to +125°C	0 to +75°C		
5-Input OR/NOR Gate	MC301	MC351	25	7.5
R-S Flip-Flop	MC302	MC352A	25	11
R-S Flip-Flop w/o Buffered Outputs	−	MC352	25	11
Half-Adder	MC303	MC353	25	7.5
Bias Driver	MC304	MC354	25	−
5-Input Gate Expander	MC305	MC355	−	4.5
3-Input OR/NOR Gate	MC306	MC356	25	7.5
3-Input OR/NOR Gate	MC307	MC357	25	7.5
AC-Coupled J-K Flip-Flop	MC308	MC358A	25	8.5
Dual 2-Input NOR Gate	MC309	MC359	25	7.0
Dual 2-Input NOR Gate	MC310	MC360	25	7.0
Dual 2-Input NOR Gate	MC311	MC361	25	7.0
Dual 3-Input NOR Gate (With Internal Bias)	MC312A	MC362A	25	7.5
Dual 3-Input NOR Gate	MC312	MC362	25	7.5
Quad 2-Input NOR Gate	MC313F	MC363F	25	7.0
AC-Coupled J-K Flip-Flop	MC314	MC364	25	12
Line Driver	MC315	MC365	−	14
Lamp Driver	MC316	MC366	−	−
Level Translator − MECL to Saturated Logic	MC317	MC367	7 DTL	27.5
Level Translator − Saturated Logic to MECL	MC318	MC368	25 ECL	17
Dual 4-Input Clock Driver/High-Speed Gate	−	MC369F	100	3.0
Dual 2-Input Clock Driver/High-Speed Gate	−	MC369G	100	3.0

Fig. 1.6 ECL1 list of products

MC1000 Series (0 to +75°C)
MC1200 Series (−55 to +125°C)

FUNCTIONS AND CHARACTERISTICS ($V_{CC} = 0$, $V_{EE} = -5.2$ V, $T_A = 25°C$)

Function	Type −55 to + 125°C	Type 0 to + 75°C	Loading Factor Each Output	Propagation Delay ns typ
Single 6-Input Gate, 3 OR Outputs w/Pulldowns, 3 NOR Outputs w/Pulldowns	MC1201F,L	MC1001P	25	4.0
Single 6-Input Gate, 3 OR Outputs w/Pulldowns, 3 NOR Outputs w/o Pulldowns	MC1202L	MC1002P	25	4.0
Single 6-Input Gate, 3 OR Outputs w/o Pulldowns, 3 NOR Outputs w/o Pulldowns	MC1203L	MC1003P	25	4.0
Dual 4-Input Gate, 2 OR Outputs w/Pulldowns, 2 NOR Outputs w/Pulldowns	MC1204F,L	MC1004P	25	4.0
Dual 4-Input Gate, 2 OR Outputs w/Pulldowns, 2 NOR Outputs w/o Pulldowns	MC1205L	MC1005P	25	4.0
Dual 4-Input Gate, 2 OR Outputs w/o Pulldowns, 2 NOR Outputs w/o Pulldowns	MC1206F,L	MC1006P	25	4.0
Triple 3-Input Gate, 3 NOR Outputs w/Pulldowns	MC1207F,L	MC1007P	25	4.0
Triple 3-Input Gate, 1 NOR Outputs w/Pulldowns, 2 NOR Outputs w/Pulldowns	MC1208L	MC1008P	25	4.0
Triple 3-Input Gate, 3 NOR Outputs w/o Pulldowns	MC1209L	MC1009P	25	4.0
Quad 2-Input Gate, 4 NOR Outputs w/Pulldowns	MC1210F,L	MC1010P	25	4.5
Quad 2-Input Gate, 2 NOR Outputs w/Pulldowns, 2 NOR Outputs w/o Pulldowns	MC1211F,L	MC1011P	25	4.5
Quad 2-Input Gate, 4 NOR Outputs w/o Pulldowns	MC1212F,L	MC1012P	25	4.5
AC Coupled J-K Flip-Flop (85 MHz typ)	MC1213F,L	MC1013P	25	6.0
Dual R-S Flip-Flop (Positive Clock)	MC1214F,L	MC1014P	25	6.0
Dual R-S Flip-Flop (Negative Clock)	MC1215F,L	MC1015P	25	6.0
Dual R-S Flip-Flop (Single Rail)	MC1216F,L	MC1016P	25	6.0
Level Translator (Saturated Logic to MECL)	MC1217F,L	MC1017P	25 (MECL)	15
Level Translator (MECL to Saturated Logic)	MC1218F,L	MC1018P	7 (DTL)	19
Full Adder	MC1219F,L	MC1019P	25	3.0 to 8.0
Quad Line Receiver	MC1220F,L	MC1020P	25	4.0
Full Subtractor	MC1221F,L	MC1021P	25	4.0 to 11
Type D Flip-Flop	MC1222F,L	MC1022P	25	8.0
Dual 4-Input OR/NOR Clock Driver	MC1223F,L	MC1023P	25	2.0
Dual 2-Input Expandable Gate	MC1224L	MC1024P	25	4.0
Dual 4 and 5-Input Expander	MC1225F,L	MC1025P	–	–
Dual 3-4-Input Transmission Line and Clock Driver	MC1226F,L	MC1026P	25	2.0
AC Coupled J-K Flip-Flop (120 MHz typ)	MC1227F,L	MC1027P	25	4.0
Dual 4-Channel Data Selector	MC1228F,L	MC1028P	25	5.0
Quad Exclusive OR Gate	MC1230F,L	MC1030P	25	5.0
Quad Exclusive NOR Gate	MC1231F,L	MC1031P	25	5.0
100-MHz AC Coupled Dual J-K Flip Flop	MC1232F,L	MC1032P	25	4.5
Dual R-S Flip Flop (Single Rail, Negative Clock)	MC1233F,L	MC1033P	25	6.0
Type D Flip-Flop	MC1234F,L	MC1034P	25	4.0
Triple Line Receiver	MC1235F,L	MC1035P	25	5.0
16-Bit Coincident Memory	MC1236F,L	MC1036P	5	17
16-Bit Coincident Memory, w/o Pulldowns	MC1237F,L	MC1037P	5	17
Quad Level Translator (MECL to Saturated Logic)	MC1239F,L	MC1039P	7 (DTL)	12
Quad Latch	MC1240F,L	MC1040P	25	8.0
Decoder - Display Driver	MC1245F,L	MC1045P	–	–
Quad 2-Input AND Gates	MC1247F,L	MC1047P	25	5.0
Quad 2-Input NAND Gates	MC1248F,L	MC1048P	25	5.0
Dual Full Adder	MC1259F,L	MC1059P	25	9.0
Quad 2-Input NOR Gate	MC1262F,L	MC1062P	25	2.0
Quad 2-Input NOR Gate	MC1263L	MC1063P	25	2.0
Triple Line Receiver	MC1266F,L	MC1066P	25	2.0
Quad MTTL to MECL Translator With Strobe	MC1267F,L	MC1067P	1	5.0
Quad MECL to MTTL Translator With Totem-Pole Outputs	MC1268F,L	MC1068P	10 (MTTL)	5.0
Quad Latch	MC1270F,L	MC1070P	25	8.0

Fig. 1.7 ECL2 list of products

package and about six external components can be used to construct even a crystal controlled oscillator.

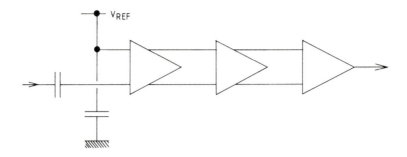

Fig. 1.8 Using the MC/SP1035 as a 100 MHz amplifier

Some manufacturers, notably Plessey, concentrated their development effort to produce some of these functions in a more convenient way. They introduced a range of flip-flops specifically for frequency division and measurement (SP600 series), see fig. 1.9.

The ECL3 (1600 series) was introduced in 1969. It was based on a 1 GHz bipolar process which is still today one of the best in general production although it does require a high supply current. Propagation delays of 1 ns made ECL3 very attractive to the instrumentation market and this was helped by the availability within the product range of oscillators, amplifiers and comparators. The penalty of high speed meant problems of layout; fast rise and fall times meant that ground plane boards and terminated transmission lines became almost essential. Sadly, ECL3 never successfully penetrated the computer market and thus the product range is limited to a small number of popular SSI circuits and special functions which are not likely to be in production beyond 1990.

For new designs the newer ECL10K family should be considered first; it is cheaper, easier to use and more widely available, although not as fast.

SP601 A & B 150 MHz

GENERAL DESCRIPTION

The SP601 is a fixed ratio emitter coupled logic ÷4 counter with a maximum specified input frequency of 150 MHz. but with a typical maximum operating frequency well in excess of this (see Typical Operating Characteristics). The operating temperature range is specified by the final coding letter: A denotes −55°C to +125°C, and B denotes 0°C to +70°C.

The SP601 can be operated with single input drive or with double, complementary, input drive. It can be driven with direct coupling from ECL II levels (or from an SP602 series device), or it can be capacitively coupled to the signal source if an external bias is provided.

There are complementary free collector outputs that can have their external load resistor connected to any bias up to 12 volts more positive than V_{EE}.

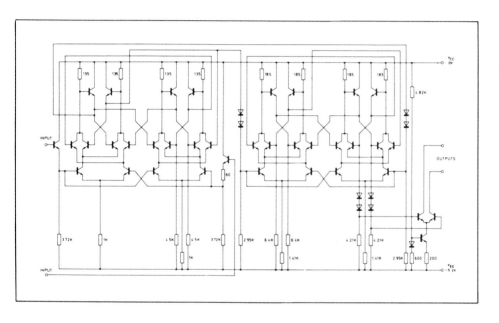

Fig. 1.9 Plessey SP601 (now replaced)

CHAPTER 2
ECL3

Fig. 2.1 ECL3 list of products

Functions and characteristics ($V_{CC} = 0$. $V_{EE} = -5.2$ V. $T_A = 25°$)

Function	Type	Loading factor each output High Z	Low Z	Propagation delay 50 Ω load ns typ
Voltage controlled oscillator	MC1648	–	–	*225 MHz typ
Dual A/D comparator	MC1650	70	7	3.5
Dual A/D comparator	MC1651	70	7	2.5
Binary counter (High Z)	MC1654	70	7	*325 MHz typ
Voltage-controlled multivibrator	MC1658	70	7	*150 MHz typ
Dual 4-input OR/NOR gate (High Z)	MC1660	70	7	1.1
Dual 4-input OR/NOR gate (Low Z)	MC1661	70	7	1.1
Quad 2-input NOR gate (High Z)	MC1662	70	7	1.1
Quad 2-input NOR gate (Low Z)	MC1663	70	7	1.1
Quad 2-input OR gate (High Z)	MC1664	70	7	1.1
Quad 2-input OR gate (Low Z)	MC1665	70	7	1.1
Dual clocked R-S flip-flop (High Z)	MC1666	70	7	1.8
Dual clocked R-S flip-flop (Low Z)	MC1667	70	7	1.8
Dual clocked latch (High Z)	MC1668	70	7	1.8
Dual clocked latch (Low Z)	MC1669	70	7	1.8
Master-slave type D flip-flop (High Z)	MC1670	70	7	*350 MHz typ
Master-slave type D flip-flop (Low Z)	MC1671	70	7	*350 MHz typ
Triple 2-input exclusive OR gate (High Z)	MC1672	70	7	1.3
Triple 2-input exclusive OR gate (Low Z)	MC1673	70	7	1.3
Triple 2-input exclusive NOR gate (High Z)	MC1674	70	7	1.3
Triple 2-input exclusive NOR gate (Low Z)	MC1675	70	7	1.3
Bi-quinary counter (High Z)	MC1678	70	7	*350 MHz typ
Bi-quinary counter (Low Z)	MC1679	70	7	*350 MHz typ
Random access memory (RAM) cell (High Z)	MC1680	70	7	Read Delay 2.5 Write Delay 3.5
Content addressable memory (CAM) cell (High Z)	MC1682	70	7	Search Delay 2.8 Write Delay 4.0
Content addressable random access (CARAM) memory cell (High Z)	MC1684	70	7	Read Delay 2.5 Search Delay 2.8 Write Delay 4.0
Dual 4-5 input OR/NOR gate (High Z)	MC1688	70	7	1.1
UHF prescaler type D flip-flop	MC1690	70	7	*500 MHz Min
Quad line receiver	MC1692	70	7	1.1
4-bit shift register (High Z)	MC1694	70	7	*325 MHz typ

*toggle frequency

ECL3 is one of the fastest logic families in production today. It is compatible with ECL10K, the more popular family, but requires more care in the design of the printed circuit board layout because the rise and fall times of the logic levels are extremely fast. Many designers use a small number of ECL3 products to boost the speed in critical parts of a 10K system. Other ECL3 products are used on a 'stand alone' basis in analogue to digital converters and frequency synthesisers. The range of ECL3 products available is shown in fig. 2.1.

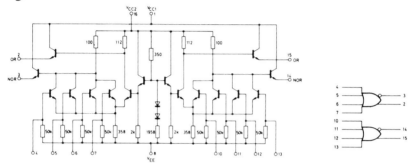

Fig. 2.2 MC/SP1660 gate

All ECL3 gates are of a similar design with a common reference voltage feeding one side of a differential amplifier. The reference varies with temperature, altering the logic levels, but the variation is cancelled by an equal and opposite effect to keep the emitter current constant. The most popular gate function is the 1660, a dual 4 input OR/NOR gate. Its circuit is shown in fig. 2.2. The simplified circuit of fig. 2.3 illustrates operation more clearly.

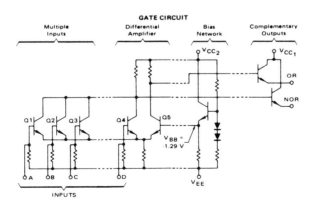

Fig. 2.3 ECL3 gate operation

The simplified circuit consists of a differential amplifier Q_1, Q_2 and a voltage regulator Q_3. The base of Q_3 is held at -2.01 V plus two diode voltage drops; the emitter-base junction voltage V_{BE} compensates for one of these so the actual reference voltage V_{ref}, is -1.29 V at 25°C, -1.23 V at 85°C and -1.35 V at -30°C. The emitter voltages of Q_1 and Q_2 are compensated by a further V_{BE} and hence the emitter current of the differential amplifier is stabilised against temperature variations. The supply current is almost constant, regardless of input levels or temperature and this is an important circuit feature. Allowing for finite values of contact resistance the voltage gain of Q_1 is just over 4 times, so that an input voltage change from -1.4 V to -1.2 V gives sufficient output voltage swing. Emitter followers (see fig. 2.2) are added to buffer the amplifier and provide sufficient output drive, if necessary, for 50 Ω transmission lines. These have separate V_{CC} connections to minimise cross-coupling.

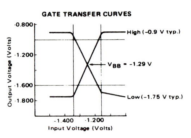

Fig. 2.4 ECL3 input/output voltage relationship

The relationship between input and output voltages at 25°C is shown in fig. 2.4 and assumes that the output pins are suitably loaded with a pulldown resistor to V_{EE}.

The voltage levels specified for operation in a system are as follows:

	-30°C	$+85$°C
V_{IH} max (max high level input voltage)	-0.875	-0.700
V_{IH} min (min high level input voltage)	-1.180	-1.025
V_{IL} max (max low level input voltage)	-1.515	-1.440
V_{IL} min (min low level input voltage)	-1.890	-1.830
V_{OH} max (max high level output voltage)	-0.875	-0.700
V_{OH} min (min high level output voltage)	-1.045	-0.890
V_{OL} max (max low level output voltage)	-1.650	-1.575
V_{OL} min (min low level output voltage)	-1.890	-1.830

These levels are compatible with ECL10K and this means that apart from the constraints of speed it is possible to mix these two ECL families on one board.

The circuit of fig. 2.2 shows one further feature – the multiple input. By providing a number of base connections to the input transistor, the circuit responds to a voltage increase (from V_{IL} to V_{IH}) on any number of inputs, thus providing the OR function. Note that since all inputs are pulled down to V_{EE} through a high value resistor (50 kΩ) on the chip, any unused inputs can be left open. Although the input voltage may then be below the specified V_{IL} min this is quite acceptable and performance is unaffected.

Some ECL3 parts have been available with 2 kΩ pulldown resistors instead of 50 kΩ so that the pulldown doubles as an output load. This restricts their flexibility and as a result they are no longer in production. These parts were identified with odd numbers (1661 to 1675) and are otherwise similar to the corresponding even numbered parts (1660 to 1674).

The output stage is invariably complementary, providing an OR/NOR function through unloaded emitter followers. For best performance both outputs should ideally be terminated (to minimise the change in supply current between logic states) using the same value of load resistor. ECL3 is specified rather strangely with loads of 50 Ω to −2 V, but this is primarily to minimise power dissipation and provide a standard impedance for measuring equipment (in fact ECL3 is normally measured with supplies of +3.2 V and −2.0 V for greater simplicity). Assuming that a single −5.2 V supply is to be used, the choice of output load covers the range from 270 Ω to 2000 Ω, although two resistors can be used (82 Ω to V_{CC}, 130 Ω to V_{EE}) to produce a 50 Ω equivalent output. The choice of output load depends mainly on the length of the connection between output and following inputs and this will be examined in more detail, but thermal considerations are also important.

ECL3 is specified for operation from −30°C to +85°C ambient but with forced air cooling which has the effect of reducing the thermal resistance (junction to ambient) from 100°C/W to 50°C/W, so halving the internal temperature rise. Cooling is certainly a good idea if a large ECL system is being constructed as lead lengths must be kept short and packages tend to be close together. Forced air cooling allows the circuitry to operate at a lower temperature and avoids 'hot spots' where the noise margins are reduced because of shifts in logic voltage levels due to overheating. Fortunately there are relatively few new requirements for this type of design; ECL3 does not offer sufficiently high levels of integration and now tends only to be used for the most speed-critical parts of equipment. Either ECL10K or logic arrays can be used for the rest. Heatsinking is still a possibility but even this is not needed if sufficient care is taken in the design and the ambient temperature does not exceed 70°C.

To calculate the temperature rise of a chip we need to know:

(a) the thermal resistance between chip and ambient (approximately 100°C/W for ECL3);
(b) the power dissipation (approximately 130 mW to 300 mW).

The chip temperature is then the product of these two (15°C to 30°C) plus the surrounding temperature. Remember that (a) can be reduced by means of heatsinking or cooling.

When the power dissipation is calculated an allowance must be made for the output loading as shown in fig. 2.5.

Fig. 2.5 ECL3 power dissipation in output load

Resistor network	Output transistor dissipation	Resistor dissipation
50 Ω to -2 V	15 mW	13 mW
2000 Ω to V_{EE}	3 mW	8 mW
1000 Ω to V_{EE}	5 mW	15 mW
270 Ω to V_{EE}	18 mW	57 mW
82 Ω to V_{CC} and 130 Ω to V_{EE}	15 mW	140 mW

So far nothing has been said about the value of load resistor to be used. This is not an easy subject but the following notes should prove helpful. ECL3 is primarily intended for use on double-sided printed circuit boards, normally with one side acting as a ground plane (V_{CC}). There are five common methods of interconnecting outputs and inputs:

(a) Direct connection of one output to one input. The maximum length of connection is 2.5 cm. The pulldown resistor can be connected anywhere and values between 1 kΩ and 2 kΩ are suitable.

(b) Direct connection but through a series damping resistor of

10 Ω to 100 Ω. The maximum length of connection is 10 cm or more but the pulldown resistor must be connected close to the output pin. Suitable values are 470 Ω to 2 kΩ. Each input (if there are more than one) requires a separate damping resistor.

(c) Wired-OR outputs. Two or more outputs are directly connected together. Unless absolutely necessary the outputs should be of functions on a single chip. Subsequent connections to input/s can use any of the techniques. These are shown diagrammatically in fig. 2.6.

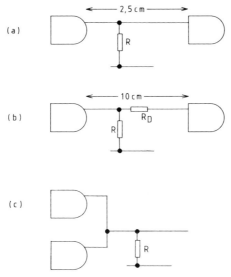

Fig. 2.6 Interconnecting ECL3 (a) R = 1 kΩ to 2 kΩ (b) R = 0.5 kΩ to 2 kΩ, R_D = 10 Ω to 100 Ω (c) Wired-OR; 2 or more outputs of a single package only

(d) Ribbon cable (or twisted pair). A push-pull output taken from any ECL3 circuit can be transmitted through flat ribbon or twisted cable (or even coax – but that costs more) for 5 metres without degradation. The 1692 line receiver must be used as shown in fig. 2.7 and propagation delays of 5½ ns per metre length will be experienced.

(e) Transmission lines. An ECL3 input appears as a relatively high resistance in parallel with a capacitance of 3 pF. This means that only six inputs can be driven from one output before the deterioration in rise and fall times becomes significant. By using a special type of PC board interconnection, creating a transmission line to connect them, the problem can be avoided. Transmission lines are also useful when the four

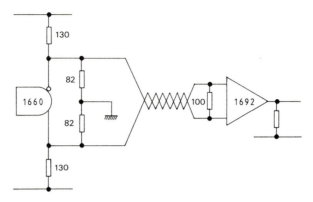

Fig. 2.7 Using the MC/SP1692 line receiver

other techniques of interconnection (already described) are not suitable. The disadvantages are that more power is consumed due to the lower values of load resistance needed and that propagation delay is increased.

The type of transmission line used on (epoxy glass) double-sided printed circuit board is known as 'microstrip'. Integrated circuits are normally mounted on the ground plane (0 v) side of the board and the microstrip lines on the other side. The lines consist of tracks of defined width which, in conjunction with the epoxy glass dielectric, present a characteristic impedance. Figure 2.8 shows a cross-section of a microstrip line together with a formula and graph to calculate the dimensions required for impedances up to 150 Ω.

Normally used values of line impedance are between 50 Ω and 100 Ω; values greater than this are difficult to achieve because the PC board tracks become too narrow. A complication arises if a transmission line is short or heavily loaded; the line impedance falls if the load capacitance becomes significant when compared to the intrinsic capacitance of the line. As a rule of thumb, 'significant' means a load capacitance greater than one ECL3 load per 5 cm of line (for a 50 Ω system) or 10 cm of line (for a 100 Ω system); these loads cause a reduction in line impedance of approximately 20%.

The graph of fig. 2.9 illustrates the impedance change with the ratio of load capacitance to line capacitance. To use the graph a figure of load capacitance per cm of line is needed for C_D.

The propagation delay along a microstrip line is approximately 0.06 ns/cm but increases with load capacitance according to the graph of fig. 2.10.

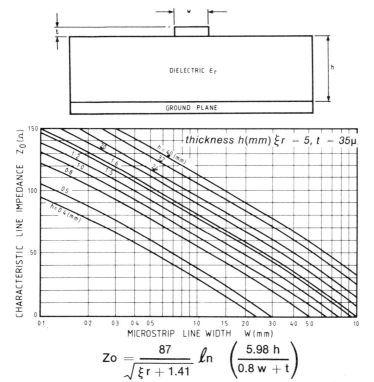

$$Zo = \frac{87}{\sqrt{\xi r + 1.41}} \; \ell n \left(\frac{5.98\,h}{0.8\,w + t} \right)$$

Fig. 2.8 Impedance of microstrip lines (unloaded)

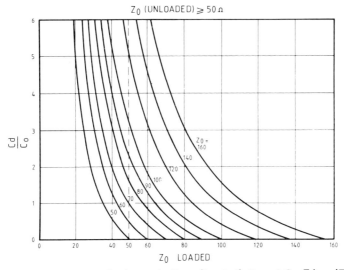

Fig. 2.9 Impedance of microstrip lines (loaded) Co = 1.2 pF/cm (Zo = 50 Ω)
0.6 pF/cm (Zo = 100 Ω)

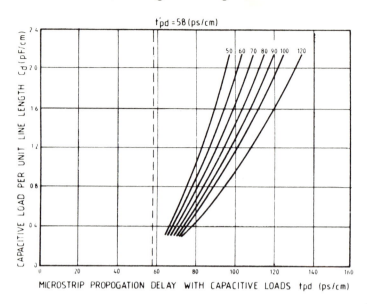

Fig. 2.10 Propagation delay of microstrip lines

Having now described the design of microstrip transmission lines it remains to explain how they are used. There are two principal configurations — series and parallel termination — as shown in fig. 2.11.

Series terminated lines can only be used for direct connection between two points. Each point can be connected to more than one line, but no connection can be made to the line except to one end. The driving device is loaded in the normal way (see table 2.1) with a resistance R_E of between 50 Ω and 10 times the line impedance. A value of 470 Ω is suitable for a single 50 Ω line. A series resistance R_S of a few ohms less than the line impedance matches the microstrip line to the driving device. When more than one line is connected to an output then each requires a series resistor. In this case it is a good idea to reduce the value of R_E by a factor corresponding to the number of driven lines (but R_E must not be less than 50 Ω).

Parallel terminated lines have an advantage over series in that connections may be made at any point along the line provided that the 'stub' lengths are less than 2 or 3 cm. Only one 50 Ω line can be driven from one output, however, and the output load resistor must correspond to the line impedance. Either a single resistor or two resistor combination can be used, and only one load is used for each line.

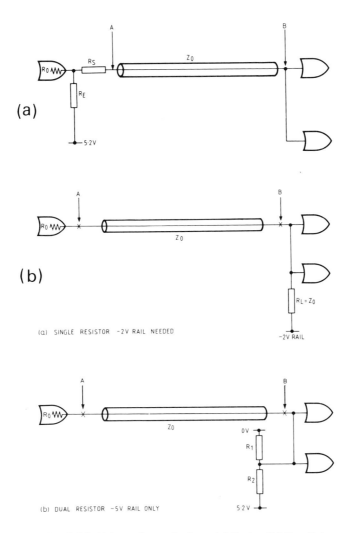

Fig. 2.11 Using microstrip lines (a) Series (b) Parallel

ECL3 product range

There seems little point in giving a detailed description of each product in the range since data sheets are available from both manufacturers. The best gate circuit to choose is undoubtedly the 1660 dual 4 input OR/NOR gate since the others do not have complementary outputs and are less popular. The most successful flip-flop is the 1670 D-type which is often used as a 300 MHz divide-by-two function. The 1692 quad line receiver is another useful circuit. There are, however, three products which are widely used as stand-alone circuits and these will now be described.

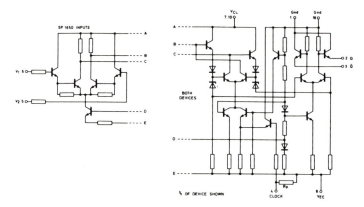

Fig. 2.12 MC/SP1650 circuit diagram (only half shown)

The 1650 is a dual voltage comparator with output latch. An alternative version, the 1651, offers the same function but with a modified input stage design capable of better performance. Since almost all current production of the 1650 meets the alternative specification the 1651 is no longer in volume production. The circuit diagram of the 1650 is shown in fig. 2.12.

Typical Transfer Curves

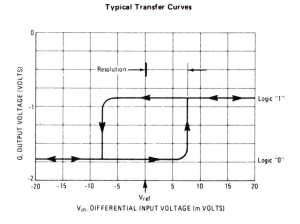

Fig. 2.13 MC/SP1650 hysteresis

The 1650 requires a dual voltage supply of +5, −5.2 V and senses input voltages of approximately 0 V (−2.5 V to +2.5 V). In normal operation the inverting input is connected to a reference voltage in this range and the non-inverting input to a variable input voltage. When the input exceeds the reference by approximately 20 mV the output Q is high. If the input is reduced to 20 mV below the reference the output level changes within a few nano-seconds. The output state can be 'frozen' by application of a 0 clock level; this feature is normally used when you need to know the logic state at a specific time.

During the uncertainty region of signal input level (± 20 mV from the reference) the logic state is automatically frozen by the addition of hysteresis to avoid the problem of oscillation. Fig. 2.13 illustrates this point.

The 1648 is a voltage controlled oscillator capable of operation up to 200 MHz. It can operate from either +5 or −5.2 V and requires an external varicap diode to change frequency. A typical application is shown in fig. 2.14.

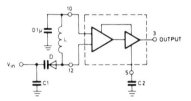

Fig. 2.14 MC/SP1648 used as a VCO

Positive feedback within the circuit maintains oscillation at the resonant frequency of the coil L and varicap tuning diode. As the voltage applied to the diode is increased, the capacitance falls, increasing the frequency of oscillation. A useful frequency range of 3:1 is readily obtained, the internal gain control circuitry ensuring a constant output amplitude of normal ECL3 level. Above 100 MHz the amplitude begins to fall and voltage level adjustments are sometimes required.

The 1648 has many applications as a clock generator, synthesiser VCO and low power transmitter.

The 1658 provides a function similar to that of the 1648 but by means of a multivibrator oscillator. Only one external timing component is needed (a capacitor) and variation of the control voltage from 0 V to −2 V gives a frequency change of at least 3 to 1. A single −5.2 V supply is needed and oscillator frequencies of 130 MHz can be achieved − figure 2.15 illustrates this.

Many other functions can be achieved using circuits in different ways. The 1692 line receiver, for example, makes a useful Schmitt trigger which can operate at 200 MHz; see fig 2.16.

The 1660 gate function can also be used as a wideband

amplifier. When the circuit is arranged as in fig. 2.17 the −3 dB point is around 500 MHz and voltage gain approximately four times per stage.

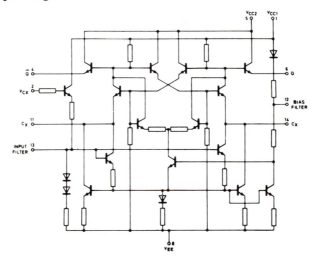

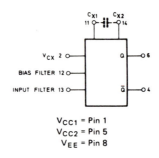

V_{CC1} = Pin 1
V_{CC2} = Pin 5
V_{EE} = Pin 8

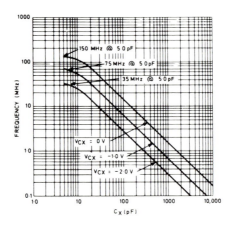

Fig. 2.15 MC/SP1658 VCM

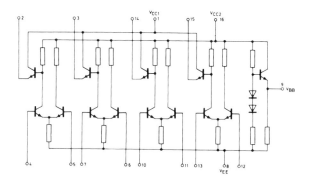

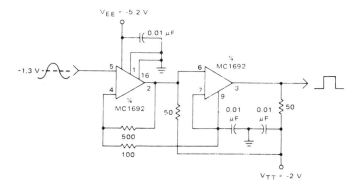

Fig. 2.16 Using the MC/SP1692 as a Schmitt trigger

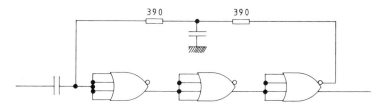

Fig. 2.17 Using the MC/SP1660 as an amplifier

CHAPTER 3
ECL10K

ECL10K is the most popular ECL family. Originally designed as an easy-to-use low speed, low power version of ECL3 for mainframe computers, the range now sells principally into the instrumentation, communications and test equipment markets. Computers have moved on to higher speed, higher density semicustom logic. The range of ECL10K products available is still increasing but table 3.1 gives a reasonable indication of what can be obtained.

ECL10K gates are of identical basic design to ECL3. Voltage levels are similar and the two ranges are compatible from that point of view. In addition there is a military temperature range version of ECL10K, the 10500/10600 series. The military range is specified with output load resistors of 100 Ω rather than 50 Ω (still to -2 volts) so there are small differences in voltage levels. Table 3.2 summarises these.

The major advantage of ECL10K over other logic families is its ease of use. Both propagation delays, and, more importantly, edge speeds have been slowed down from those of ECL3. The result is that fast logic systems can be built using ordinary double-sided (sometimes even single-sided) printed circuit boards. ECL10K can even be 'wire-wrapped'. The resultant saving in power consumption and smaller chip sizes has allowed the design of a large number of complex functions as part of the standard range. Some 10K circuits offer improved speed with higher current consumption — these fall into the 10200 series and are generally otherwise similar to the corresponding 10100 series products. Table 3.3 is a comparison of the edge and switching speeds.

The rise and fall times shown in table 3.3 are based on 10% to 90% rather than 20% to 80% normally specified for 10K.

Circuit design and layout details for 10K differ from ECL3 in two respects:

Table 3.1 Range of ECL10K products

Function	Device -30 to +85°C	Function	Device -30 to +85°C
NOR gates		*Translators*	
Quad 2-input gate/strobe	10100	Quad TTL-MECL	10124
Quad 2-input gate	10102	Quad MECL-TTL	10125
Triple 4-3-3 input gate	10106	Triple MECL-MOS	10177
Dual 3-input 3-output gate	10111	Quad MST to MECL	10190
Dual 3-input 3-output gate	10211	Hex MECL-MST	10191
OR gates		*Flip-flop/latches*	
Quad 2-input gate	10103	Dual D master slave flip-flop	10131
Dual 3-input 3-output gate	10110	Dual J-K master slave flip-flop	10135
Dual 3-input 3-output gate	10210	Hex D master slave flip-flop	10176
AND gates		Hex D common reset flip-flop	10186
Quad 2-input gate	10104	Dual D master slave flip-flop	10231
Hex gate	10197	Quad latch	10133
Complex gates		Quint latch	10175
Quad OR/NOR gate	10101	Quad/common clock latch	10168
Triple 2-3-2 input OR/NOR gate	10105	Quad/negative clock latch	10153
Dual 4-5 input OR/NOR gate	10109	Dual latch	10130
Dual 3-input 3-output OR/NOR gate	10212	*Multiplexer*	
Triple 2-input exclusive OR/NOR gate	10107	Quad 2-input/non-inverting	10158
Quad 2-input exclusive OR/NOR gate	10113	Dual multiplexer/latch	10132
		Dual multiplexer/latch	10134
Dual 2-wide 2-3 input OR-AND/OR-AND invert	10117	Quad 2-input/inverting	10159
Dual 2-wide 3-input OR-AND	10118	8-line	10164
4-wide 4-3-3-3 input OR-AND	10119	Quad 2-input/latch	10173
4-wide 3-input OR-AND/OR-AND-invert	10121	Dual 4-1	10174
Buffers/inverters		*Encoders*	
Hex buffer/enable	10188	8-input encoder	10165
Hex inverter/enable	10189	*Decoders*	
Hex inverter/buffer	10195	Binary to 1-8 (low)	10161
Line drivers/line receivers		Binary to 1-8 (high)	10162
Triple line receiver	10114	Dual binary to 1-4 (low)	10171
Quad line receiver	10115	Dual binary to 1-4 (high)	10172
Triple line receiver	10116	*Parity generator/checkers*	
Quad bus receiver	10129	12-bit parity generator-checker	10160
Quad bus driver	10192	9 + 2 bit parity	10170
Triple line receiver	10216	*Error detector/correction*	
Triple 4-3-3 input bus driver	10123	IBM code	10163
Dual bus driver	10128	Motorola code	10193
Dual transceiver	10194		

(a) there are more LSI and MSI functions;

(b) transmission (microstrip) line interconnections are no longer so necessary.

Table 3.2 Voltage levels related to temperature

	−55°C	−30°C	+85°C	+125°C
V_{IH} max (max high level input voltage)	−0.880	−0.890	−0.700	−0.630
V_{IH} min (min high level input voltage)	−1.255	−1.205	−1.035	−1.000
V_{IL} max (max low level input voltage)	−1.510	−1.500	−1.440	−1.400
V_{IL} min (min low level input voltage)	−1.920	−1.890	−1.825	−1.820
V_{OH} max (max high level output voltage)	−0.880	−0.890	−0.700	−0.630
V_{OH} min (min high level output voltage)	−1.080	−1.060	−0.890	−0.825
V_{OL} max (max low level output voltage)	−1.655	−1.675	−1.615	−1.545
V_{OL} min (min low level output voltage)	−1.920	−1.890	−1.825	−1.820

Table 3.3 Comparison of edge and switching speeds

	ECL3	ECL10100	ECL10200
Prop delay (typ)	1.0 ns	2.0 ns	1.5 ns
Prop delay (max)	1.6 ns	2.9 ns	2.5 ns
Rise time (typ)	1.3 ns	4.0 ns	3.0 ns
Fall time (typ)	1.3 ns	3.3 ns	2.5 ns

Lead lengths up to 15 cm between pins are permissible; up to 100 cm or more if a series resistor is used. For longer lengths the usual twisted, flat or coaxial cable is acceptable. Obviously it helps if the techniques outlined in chapter 2 are employed and double-sided boards with an earth plane are certainly a wise precaution.

ECL10K was introduced as a logic family by Motorola, still the major supplier. Some of the early second sources (Texas Instruments and Plessey) found it difficult to produce completely interchangeable products and the only alternative suppliers left are Fairchild and Signetics (Philips). Several other companies (e.g. in Japan) produce part of the family but principally to aid sales of related products. The numbering system has been standardised as far as possible and the following list indicates this:

Number	*Function*
10100 to 10109	simple gates
10110 to 10119	complex gates
10120 to 10129	interface circuits
10130 to 10135	latches, flip-flops

Number	*Function*
10136 to 10139	counters
10140 to 10179	various MSI functions
10180 to 10183	adders, multipliers
10184 to 10194	interface circuits
10195 to 10197	gates
10198	multivibrator
10200 to 10209	simple gates
10210 to 10219	complex gates
10220 to 10299	as 10120-10199

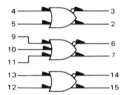

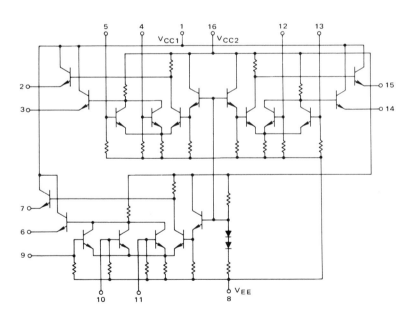

Fig. 3.1 10105 simple gate

ECL10K offers a relatively small number of gate functions compared, say, with TTL. But by using the wired-OR and dual output features inherent in ECL and noting that all functions can drive a 50 Ω line (so almost every ECL10K function is a line driver) the range becomes more than adequate. A typical popular simple gate circuit is the 10105, shown in fig. 3.1. It is a triple gate consisting of a single 3 input and two dual input OR/NOR functions.

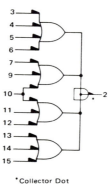

*Collector Dot

Fig. 3.2 10119 OR/AND gate

Some gates have so many inputs and outputs that it is difficult to describe their configuration simply. A convention has been introduced to simplify this, and the device shown as an example in fig. 3.2 is known as a 4-wide 4-3-3-3 input OR/AND gate.

Several types of gate circuit are worthy of special mention. The 10110 is a dual 3 output gate (all the same polarity) intended for clock distribution. An inverse polarity version is also produced. The 10110 is shown in fig. 3.3.

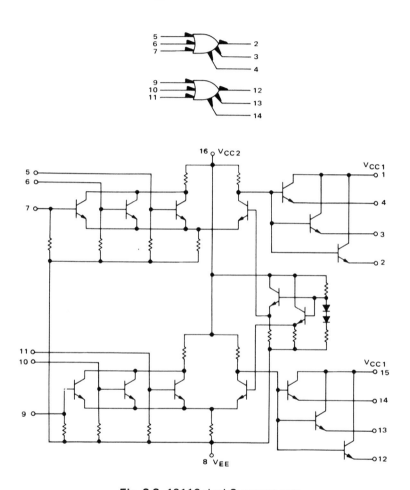

Fig. 3.3 10110 dual 3 output gate

Although line driving is easy in ECL it is still necessary to use special line receivers. The 10114, 5 and 6 are each similar in concept to the ECL3 1692 and have similar bias output pins.

Applications which require a 50 Ω ECL bus may benefit from the use of the 10123 triple bus driver, which incorporates a special switched output stage to avoid incorrect line loading. This allows several outputs to drive the same microstrip line. Fig. 3.4 shows a diagram of the 10123 and its application.

For interfacing into different logic levels there are several useful circuits. The 10125 and 10124 interface into and out of TTL, respectively. In each case they require supply voltages of +5 V and −5.2 V. Where it is necessary to drive several TTL loads (or even an NMOS memory) the 10177 can be used instead of the 10125. There are two interface circuits for a TTL bus. The 10128 driver has a three state output and internal latch for this purpose and the corresponding latched receiver, the 10129, provides hysteresis to deal with any line reflections. It is also possible to interface ECL10K to many other types of high speed data bus, including a special ECL bus driven from open collector outputs. The 10192 and 4 are used for this, the latter being a dual transceiver as shown in fig. 3.5.

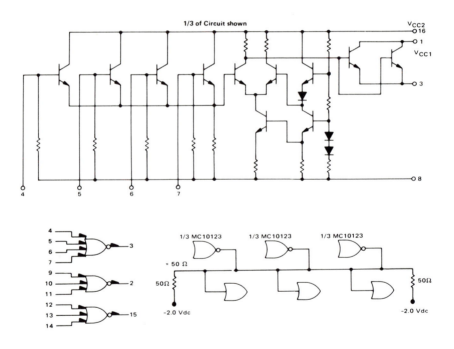

Fig. 3.4 10123 triple bus driver

Although latches are often integrated into more complex functions ECL10K offers both dual (10130) and quad (10133, 10153 and 10168) latches. A simplified quint latch, the 10175 is also available and is shown in fig. 3.6.

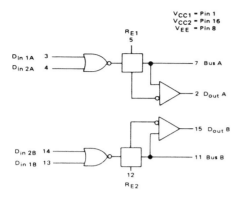

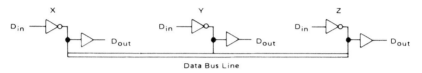

Fig. 3.5 10194 dual bus transceiver

TRUTH TABLE

Inputs		Outputs	
$D_{in\,1}$	$D_{in\,2}$	Bus	D_{out}
L	L	V_{Bus0}	H
H	L	V_{BusH}	H
L	H	V_{BusH}	H
H	H	V_{BusH}	H
L	L	V_{BusH}	L
H	L	V_{BusL}	L
L	H	V_{BusL}	L
H	H	V_{BusL}	L

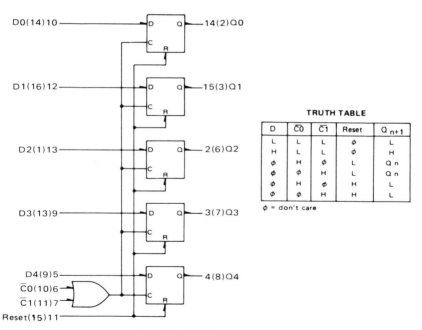

TRUTH TABLE

D	$\overline{C0}$	$\overline{C1}$	Reset	Q_{n+1}
L	L	L	ϕ	L
H	L	L	ϕ	H
ϕ	H	ϕ	L	$Q\,n$
ϕ	ϕ	H	L	$Q\,n$
ϕ	H	ϕ	H	L
ϕ	ϕ	H	H	L

ϕ = don't care

Fig. 3.6 10175 quint latch

The popular dual D type flip-flop, the 10131, is available in a higher speed version (10231) with a guaranteed toggle rate of 200 MHz instead of 125 MHz. There are now two hex D types

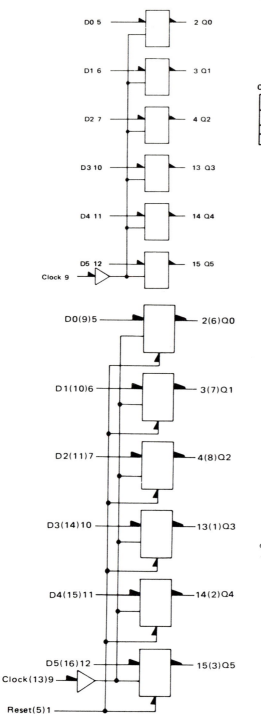

CLOCKED TRUTH TABLE

C	D	Q_{n+1}
L	ϕ	Q_n
H*	L	L
H*	H	H

ϕ = Don't Care

*A clock H is a clock transition from a low to a high state.

CLOCKED TRUTH TABLE

R	C	Q	Q_{n+1}
L	L	ϕ	Q_n
L	H *	L	L
L	H *	H	H
H	L	ϕ	L

ϕ = Don't Care

*A clock H is a clock transition from a low to a high state.

Fig. 3.7 10176/10186 hex flip-flops

SEQUENTIAL TRUTH TABLE*

INPUTS								OUTPUTS				
S1	S2	D0	D1	D2	D3	Carry In	Clock **	Q0	Q1	Q2	Q3	Carry Out
L	L	L	L	H	H	φ	H	L	L	H	H	L
L	H	φ	φ	φ	φ	L	H	H	L	H	H	H
L	L	φ	φ	φ	φ	L	H	L	H	H	H	H
L	H	φ	φ	φ	φ	L	H	H	H	H	H	L
L	H	φ	φ	φ	φ	H	L	H	H	H	H	H
L	H	φ	φ	φ	φ	H	H	H	H	H	H	H
H	H	φ	φ	φ	φ	φ	H	H	H	H	H	H
L	L	H	H	L	L	φ	H	H	H	L	L	L
H	L	φ	φ	φ	φ	L	H	L	H	L	L	H
H	L	φ	φ	φ	φ	L	H	H	L	L	L	L
H	L	φ	φ	φ	φ	L	H	L	L	L	L	L
H	L	φ	φ	φ	φ	L	H	H	H	H	H	H

φ = Don't care.
 * Truth table shows logic states assuming inputs vary in sequence shown from top to bottom.
** A clock H is defined as a clock input transition from a low to a high logic level.

V_{CC1} = Pin 1 (5) P_D = 625 mW typ/pkg (No Load)
V_{CC2} = Pin 16 (4) f_{count} = 150 MHz typ
 V_{EE} = Pin 8 (12) t_{pd} = 3.3 ns typ (C - Q)
  = 7.0 ns typ (C - $\overline{C}_{out}$)
  = 5.0 ns typ ($\overline{C}_{in}$ - $\overline{C}_{out}$)

FUNCTION SELECT TABLE

S1	S2	Operating Mode
L	L	Preset (Program)
L	H	Increment (Count Up)
H	L	Decrement (Count Down)
H	H	Hold (Stop Count)

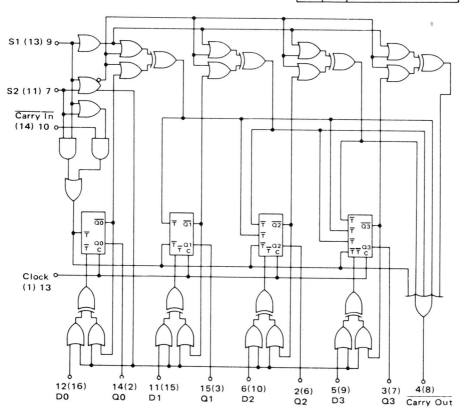

Fig. 3.8 10136 hexadecimal counter

(10176 and 10186) and these can be seen in fig. 3.7. A dual JK flip-flop is also available (10135).

Several counters are produced, the most popular being the 10136 hexadecimal and 10137 decade products. These are ideal for programmable counting up to 100 MHz or so and the logic diagram and typical applications are shown in fig. 3.8. Both products can count up or down at 125 MHz but propagation delays restrict the counting speed in some systems.

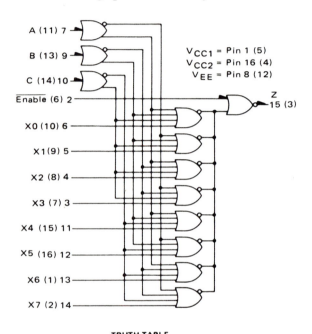

		TRUTH TABLE		
	ADDRESS INPUTS			
ENABLE	C	B	A	Z
L	L	L	L	X0
L	L	L	H	X1
L	L	H	L	X2
L	L	H	H	X3
L	H	L	L	X4
L	H	L	H	X5
L	H	H	L	X6
L	H	H	H	X7
H	φ	φ	φ	L

φ = Don't Care

Fig. 3.9 10164 8 line multiplexer

Three other counters are based on an arrangement of four cascaded flip-flops. The 10154 and 10178 (alternate polarity) have outputs at div 2, div 4, div 8 and div 16. They have a common reset and individual set facility. The 10138 is configured in a similar manner but divides by 2, 5 and 10.

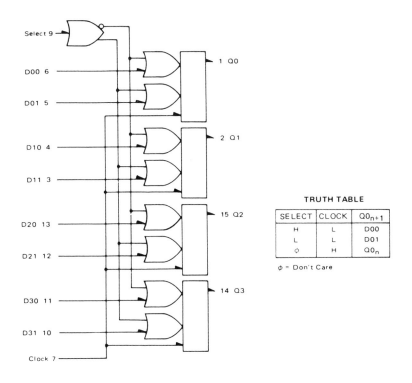

Fig. 3.10 10173 latched multiplexer

Among the various MSI functions included in the ECL10K range are a number of multiplexers, encoders and decoders which consist of several gates, with or without latches. The 10164 is a typical example of a simple 8 line multiplexer and is shown in fig. 3.9. The data is routed according to the 3 bit code supplied to the address input and a chip enable input allows the selection of one of several multiplexers when more than eight inputs are needed.

An example of a latched multiplexer is the 10173, shown in fig. 3.10. The choice here is between four lots of two inputs, and as this is a common requirement there are unlatched versions also (10158, 10159). There are also three dual multiplexers.

A typical decoder is the 10161 shown in fig. 3.11. It has three input bits and the outputs, normally at logic 1, will go low when selected. Within the range there are opposite polarity versions of this and a dual 1 of 4 decoder.

Encoding is a relatively unusual requirement in that multiplexing, gating, or a combination of both, can do this simply. The 10165, known as a 'priority encoder' behaves more like an analogue to digital converter. There are eight inputs (plus a latch input) and four outputs. When the inputs are at 0 then all outputs are at 0. When any input is high then one of the outputs (Q3) always goes high. The other outputs give the binary number corresponding to the highest number of the input (0 to 7) which is at 1. The principal application of the priority encoder is in the prioritisation of input signals — the most important inputs overriding the rest. A logic diagram appears in fig. 3.12.

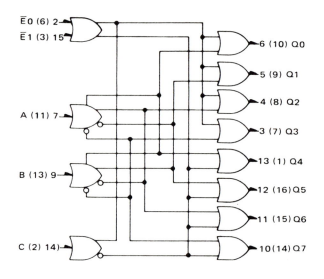

TRUTH TABLE

ENABLE INPUTS		INPUTS			OUTPUTS							
$\overline{E}1$	$\overline{E}0$	C	B	A	Q0	Q1	Q2	Q3	Q4	Q5	Q6	Q7
L	L	L	L	L	L	H	H	H	H	H	H	H
L	L	L	L	H	H	L	H	H	H	H	H	H
L	L	L	H	L	H	H	L	H	H	H	H	H
L	L	L	H	H	H	H	H	L	H	H	H	H
L	L	H	L	L	H	H	H	H	L	H	H	H
L	L	H	L	H	H	H	H	H	H	L	H	H
L	L	H	H	L	H	H	H	H	H	H	L	H
L	L	H	H	H	H	H	H	H	H	H	H	L
H	φ	φ	φ	φ	H	H	H	H	H	H	H	H
φ	H	φ	φ	φ	H	H	H	H	H	H	H	H

Fig. 3.11 10161 1-of-8 decoder

A similar type of complex gate but without latches is the parity generator/checker, a network of EX—OR gates which provides an output only when an odd (or even) number of inputs are high. ECL10K offers 12 bit odd (10160) and 9 + 2 bit odd/even parity (10170) products.

When a single error has been detected it can be corrected using a combination of these parity circuits together with either the

10163 or 10193 correction circuits. Intended for use in large memory systems incorporating check bits stored along with the required data, these devices are relatively specialised.

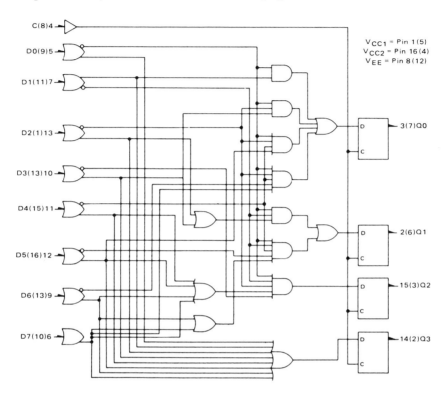

Fig. 3.12 10165 priority encoder

Only a single shift register appears in the ECL10K range – see fig. 3.13. The 10141 is a four bit register which can shift left, right and deal with serial or parallel inputs and outputs. The shift frequency is 150 MHz minimum and clocking occurs on the positive edge.

Another MSI function is the 10198 monostable multivibrator. Like TTL counterparts it is optionally retriggerable and covers several decades of timing pulse width. Fig. 3.14 illustrates how pulse width and recovery time vary with external timing components; a realistic minimum timing period is about 25 ns.

Finally, ECL10K offers an impressive range of arithmetic functions. The simplest is a magnitude comparator, the 10166, a complex gate with two sets of five inputs and two outputs as can be seen in fig. 3.15. The outputs of the comparator indicate

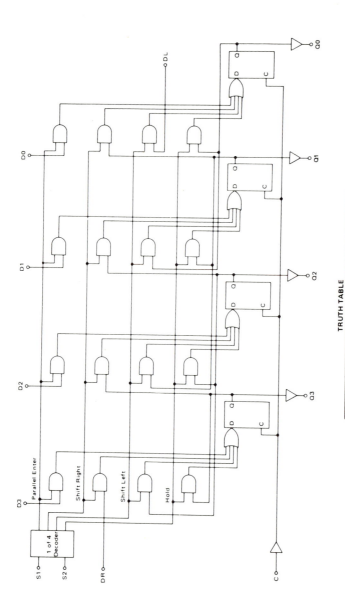

TRUTH TABLE

SELECT		OPERATING MODE	OUTPUTS			
S1	S2		$Q0_{n+1}$	$Q1_{n+1}$	$Q2_{n+1}$	$Q3_{n+1}$
L	L	Parallel Entry	D0	D1	D2	D3
L	H	Shift Right*	$Q1_n$	$Q2_n$	$Q3_n$	DR
H	L	Shift Left*	DL	$Q0_n$	$Q1_n$	$Q2_n$
H	H	Stop Shift	$Q0_n$	$Q1_n$	$Q2_n$	$Q3_n$

*Outputs as exist after pulse appears at "C" input with input conditions as shown. (Pulse = Positive transition of clock input).

Fig. 3.13 10141 shift register

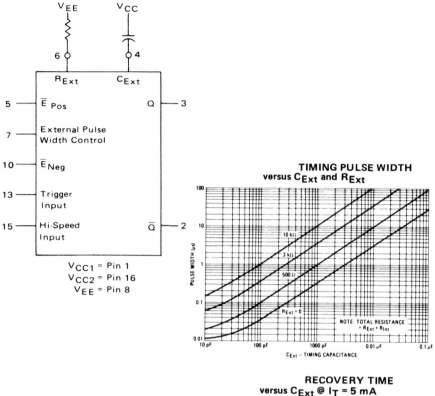

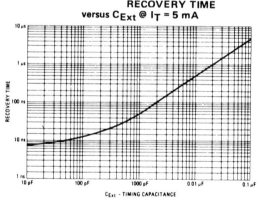

TRUTH TABLE

INPUT		OUTPUT
$\overline{E}_{Pos}$	$\overline{E}_{Neg}$	
L	L	Triggers on both positive & negative input slopes
L	H	Triggers on positive input slope
H	L	Triggers on negative input slope
H	H	Trigger is disabled

Fig. 3.14 10198 monostable multivibrator

whether the sets of inputs are equal and, if not, which corresponds to the larger binary number.

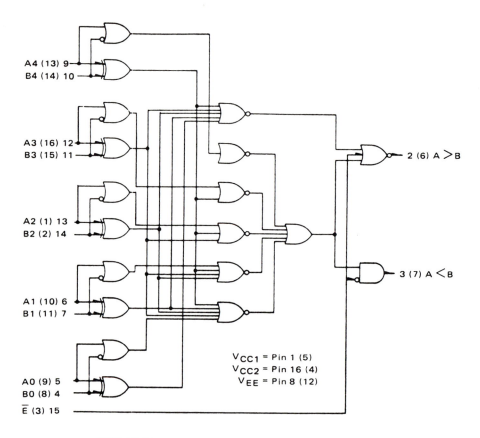

A4 (13) 9
B4 (14) 10

A3 (16) 12
B3 (15) 11

A2 (1) 13
B2 (2) 14

A1 (10) 6
B1 (11) 7

A0 (9) 5
B0 (8) 4

$\overline{E}$ (3) 15

V_{CC1} = Pin 1 (5)
V_{CC2} = Pin 16 (4)
V_{EE} = Pin 8 (12)

2 (6) A $>$ B

3 (7) A $<$ B

TRUTH TABLE

Inputs			Outputs	
$\overline{E}$	A	B	A $<$ B	A $>$ B
H	x	x	L	L
L	Word A = Word B		L	L
L	Word A $>$ Word B		L	H
L	Word A $<$ Word B		H	L

Fig. 3.15 10166 magnitude comparator

To add or subtract two 2 bit numbers the 10180 takes only 5.5 ns max. The corresponding 2 bit multiplier is the 10287 and these devices can be used together as the basis of large arrays. A higher level of integration is offered by the 10183 4 x 2 multiplier; the logic diagram of fig. 3.16 is extremely complex!

Two arithmetic logic units (ALUs) and their associated look-

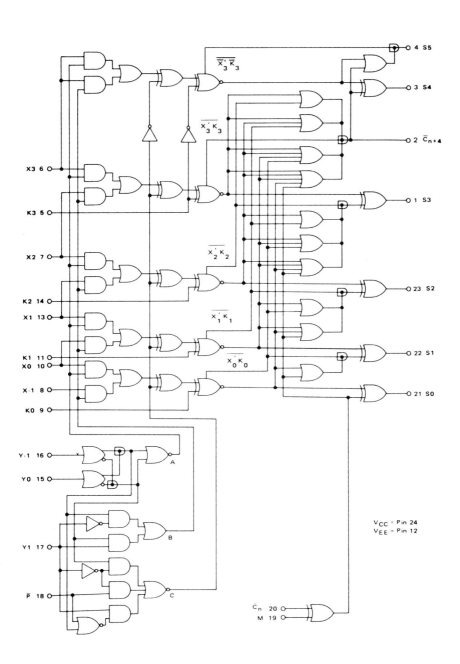

Fig. 3.16 10183 4-by-2 multiplier

ahead-carry block (10179) complete the range. The 10181 operates on two 4 bit words A0 ... A3 and B0 ... B3 according to the function select pins S0 ... S3 to produce the appropriate outputs F0 ... F3. The 10182 is a simpler version in a 16 lead package which operates on only 2 bits. Fig. 3.17 indicates the functions available within the 10181; these include addition, subtraction and multiplication.

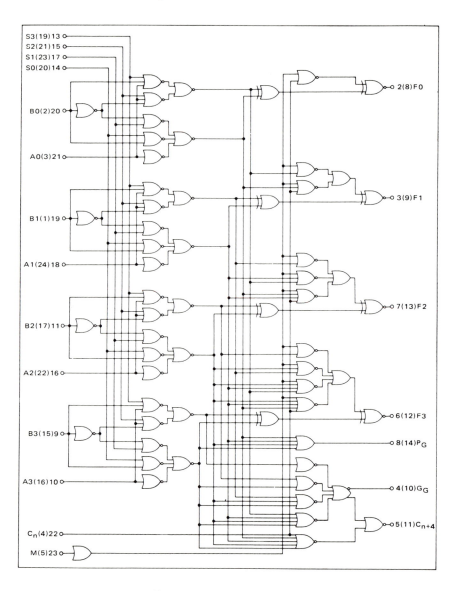

Fig. 3.17 10181 4 bit ALU

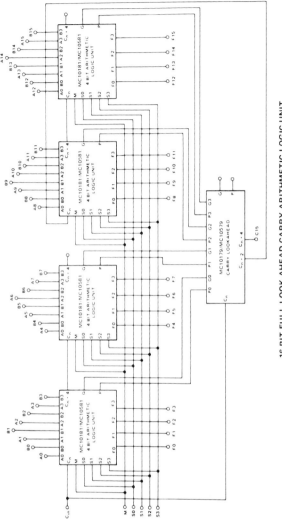

16-BIT FULL LOOK-AHEAD CARRY ARITHMETIC LOGIC UNIT

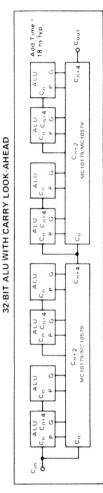

32-BIT ALU WITH CARRY LOOK-AHEAD

Fig. 3.18 Using the 10179 and 10181

Several ALUs can be connected, perhaps with a look-ahead-carry (10179), to create the basis of a fast processor. In a 32 bit system the typical time taken to add two words can be reduced from 30 ns to 18 ns using the 10179. See fig. 3.18.

This completes our summary of standard ECL10K circuits available at present. More are in development and the latest data should be consulted. The next chapter looks at the developments which have stemmed from 10K — faster, more complex products and memories.

CHAPTER 4
Extended 10K

There are five groups of products based on ECL10K which represent the forefront of the technology as far as standard logic families are concerned. These groups are as follows:

The 10500 military range
ECL10800 series processors
The 10H000 (10KH) range
The 100000 (100K) range
ECL memories

Many of the normal ECL10K products are available for use over an extended −55 to +125°C temperature range. A list of those available appears in fig. 4.1. Note that the numbering system is similar but for the addition of 400 to the type number; thus a 10158 commercial product corresponds to a 10558 military grade.

The Motorola range of 10800 series ECL processors represents a major advance in circuit design complexity from the 10K series. Power consumption has been reduced considerably, and the products compete favourably with Schottky TTL alternatives. Unlike TTL, however, it is more difficult to interface with low cost, high capacity, MOS memories. Their access time is often too great, anyway. Although ECL memories are available (with the exception of high speed ROMs) − and in fact many fast TTL RAMs use ECL memory cells internally − they are of limited capacity. A further consideration is that processor configurations normally suitable for low speed processing are not always ideal for higher speeds. This topic is examined again in a later chapter. But the 10800 series is still of considerable importance and a brief introduction now follows.

The 10800 range is based on a 4 bit arithmetic logic unit (ALU) which can be expanded by the parallel connection of more ALUs to 8, 12, 16, or more bits. This type of ALU is known as a 4 bit 'slice' for obvious reasons. At present there are six other circuits in the range and their functions are to interface the ALU to other circuitry, to control the ALU and to add extra facilities. The ALU is the 10800 and appears in block diagram form in fig. 4.2.

Fig. 4.1 ECL10K range of military products

Function	Device Type	Function	Device Type
NOR gates		*Multiplexer*	
Quad 2-input gate strobe	10500	Quad 2-input/non-inverting	10558
Quad 2-input gate	10502	Dual multiplexer/latch	10532
Triple 4-3-3 input gate	10506	Dual multiplexer/latch	10534
Dual 3-input 3-output gate	10611	Quad 2-input/inverting	10559
OR gates		8-line	10564
Quad 2-input gate	10503	Dual 4-1	10574
Dual 3-input 3-output gate	10610	*Decoders*	
AND gates		Binary to 1-8 (low)	10561
Quad 2-input gate	10504	Binary to 1-8 (high)	10562
Hex gate	10597	Dual 4-line (low)	10571
		Dual 4-line (high)	10572
Complex		*Counters*	
Quad OR/NOR gate	10501	Hexadecimal	10536
Triple 2-3-2 input OR/NOR gate	10505	Decade	10537
Dual 4-5 input OR/NOR gate	10509	Biquinary	10538
Dual 3-input 3-output OR/NOR gate	10612	Binary down counter	10554
		Binary	10578
Exclusive triple 2-input gate	10507	*Arithmetic functions*	
Exclusive quad 2-input gate	10513	12-bit parity generator	10560
Complex OR/AND gate function	10517	Error detection/correction	10563
Complex OR/AND gate function	10518	8-input priority encoder	10565
Complex OR/AND gate function	10519	5-bit magnitude comparator	10566
Complex OR/AND gate function	10521	9 + 2 bit parity checker	10570
Buffers/inverters		Look-ahead-carry block	10579
Hex inverter/buffer	10595	Dual 2-bit adder/subtractor	10580
Line drivers/line receivers		4-bit arithmetic function gen.	10581
Triple line receiver	10514	2-bit arithmetic function gen.	10582
Quad line receiver	10515	Error detection/correction	10593
Triple line receiver	10516	2-bit multiplier	10687
Triple line receiver	10616	*Translators*	
Dual transceiver	10594	Quad TTL-MECL	10524
Flip-flop/latches		Quad MECL-TTL	10525
Dual D master slave flip-flop	10531	Quad MST to MECL	10590
Dual J-K master slave flip-flop	10535	Hex MECL-MST	10591
Hex D master slave flip-flop	10576	*Special function*	
Hex D common reset flip-flop	10586	4-bit shift register	10541
Dual D master slave flip-flop	10631		
Quad latch	10533		
Quint latch	10575		
Quad/common clock latch	10568		
Quad/negative clock latch	10553		
Dual latch	10530		

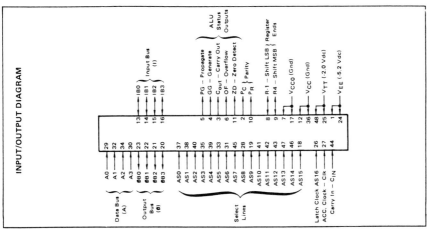

INPUT/OUTPUT DIAGRAM

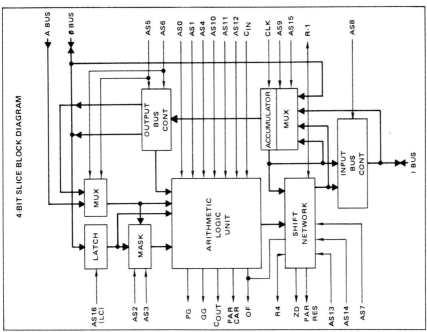

4-BIT SLICE BLOCK DIAGRAM

Fig. 4.2
10800 4 bit ALU slice

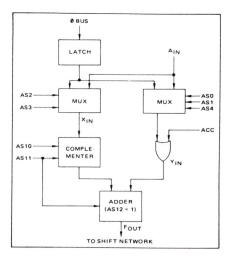

Fig. 4.3 Arithmetic instruction set of the 10800

Y MUX		X MUX		÷2	COMPLE-MENT	ACC	BINARY FUNCTION (PLUS C$_{IN}$)	BCD FUNCTION (PLUS C$_{IN}$)
AS0	AS1	AS2	AS3	AS4	AS10	$\overline{AS5}$·AS6	AS11 = 1	AS11 = 0
1	0	0	1	1	1	0	A PLUS 0	A PLUS 0
1	0	0	1	1	0	0	A PLUS $\overline{0}$	A PLUS 9's COMP. 0
0	1	1	0	1	0	0	0 PLUS $\overline{A}$	0 PLUS 9's COMP. A
0	0	1	0	1	1	0	A	A
0	0	0	1	1	1	0	0	0
0	0	1	0	1	0	0	$\overline{A}$	9's COMP. A
0	0	0	1	1	0	0	$\overline{0}$	9's COMP. 0
1	1	1	0	1	1	0	−1 PLUS A	*
1	1	0	1	1	1	0	−1 PLUS 0	*
1	1	1	0	0	1	0	−2 PLUS A	*
1	1	0	1	0	1	0	−2 PLUS 0	*
0	0	1	0	0	1	0	+2 PLUS A	+2 PLUS A
0	0	0	1	0	1	0	+2 PLUS 0	+2 PLUS 0
1	0	1	0	1	1	0	A PLUS A	A PLUS A
0	1	0	1	1	1	0	0 PLUS 0	0 PLUS 0
0	0	1	0	1	1	1	ACC PLUS A	ACC PLUS A
0	0	0	1	1	1	1	ACC PLUS 0	ACC PLUS 0
0	0	1	0	1	0	1	ACC PLUS $\overline{A}$	ACC PLUS 9's COMP. A
0	0	0	1	1	0	1	ACC PLUS $\overline{0}$	ACC PLUS 9's COMP. 0
0	0	0	0	1	1	1	ACC PLUS A·0	ACC PLUS A·0
0	0	0	0	1	0	1	ACC PLUS $\overline{A}$·$\overline{0}$	ACC PLUS 9's COMP. A·0
0	0	1	1	1	1	1	ACC PLUS A + 0	*
0	0	1	1	1	0	1	ACC PLUS $\overline{A}$ + 0	*

*Not Defined in BCD

The 10800 features three separate 4 bit data bus connections. The A bus can only be used as an input; the others are bidirectional but IB is normally used for inputs, OB for outputs. Seventeen separate select inputs determine which operations are to be performed between the bus lines; for example, the inputs AS0 and AS1 determine which bus is to be connected as one of the two ALU inputs. Other select inputs control logic functions such as add/subtract, shift left/shift right, binary/BCD etc. The 10800 is extremely flexible; the set of arithmetic functions shown in fig.

4.3 indicates the operation of only nine of these inputs to give an idea of what the circuit can do. The 10800 4 bit slice is packaged in a 48 lead quad-in-line outline and consumes 250 mA from each of two supply voltages, −5.2 V and −2 V (for terminations).

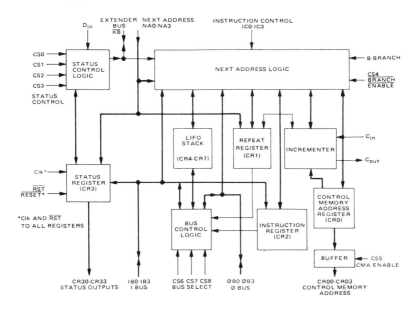

Fig. 4.4 10801 microprogram control function

Most applications of the 10800 will require the ALU to perform a sequence of operations – perhaps to obtain data from a memory location, to multiply it with data from another location and store it in a third. As it stands, the 10800 can only perform a single function according to the logic levels on the select inputs. In order to control these and provide a sequence of instructions there is a second circuit, the 10801. This is a microprogram controller, and once again is 4 bits 'wide'. A block diagram of the 10801 appears in fig. 4.4.

A detailed explanation of the operation of the 10801 can be found elsewhere. A further circuit, the 10803 memory interface, allows the other two to deal with data in memory locations instead of data on the three bus lines. This circuit is very complex as it incorporates an ALU (with almost as many instructions as the 10800) to calculate the addresses. It is possible to use this capability to extend the processing power of the 10800 (e.g. for double precision arithmetic) or even in place of the 10800, but this is not always advisable. The 10803 has connections for five data bus lines, each 4 bits wide. There are two bi-directional 'ports' — one normally for inputs, one for outputs. A further bi-directional port connects to a memory data bus. An input bus for memory 'pointers' and an output memory address bus are also accommodated. Fig. 4.5 illustrates this. The overall system configuration can be seen in fig. 4.6. Other arrangements are possible of course, and a complete processor requires additional clocks, latches and peripheral components not shown here.

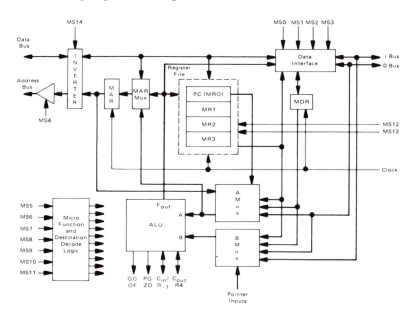

Fig. 4.5 10803 memory interface function

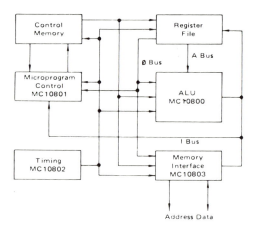

Fig. 4.6 10800 processor structure

The two remaining areas are the control memory (to store the sequence of instructions for the ALU) and a register file (to store intermediate calculations and remember overflow and similar conditions). Although these can be constructed from memory and standard ECL10K products there is a dual access stack, the 10806, which can store 32 bytes of data and buffer external ECL memory.

BLOCK DIAGRAM

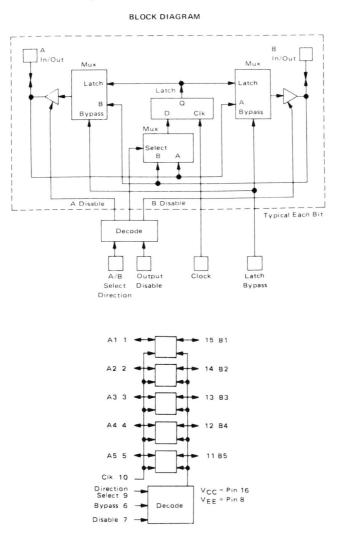

Fig. 4.7 10807 latched transceiver

Three further circuits allow the extension of the simple processor to interface with ECL, TTL or MOS systems, either to use

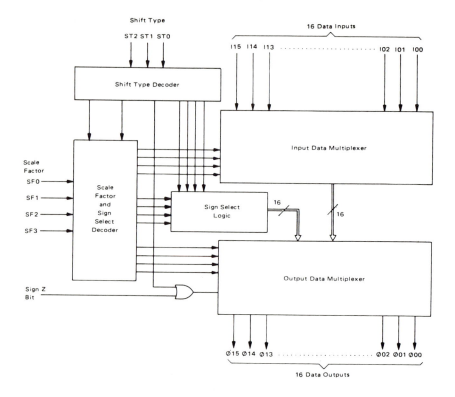

BLOCK DIAGRAM

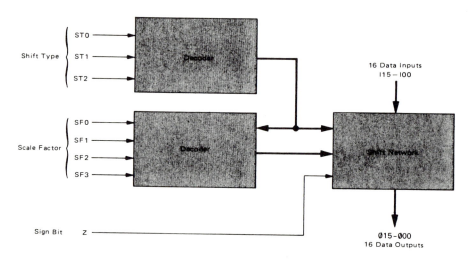

Fig. 4.8 10808 programmable shifter

cheaper memory or to connect several systems to a single bus. These circuits are as follows:

10804 4 bit TTL bus interface
10805 5 bit MOS/TTL interface
10807 5 bit ECL bus interface

A diagram of the 10807 appears in fig. 4.7; the others are similar.

Finally there is a new circuit, the 10808, which is designed to add extra features (such as floating point arithmetic) to the ALU. The 10808 is known as a programmable shifter and is 16 bits wide; see fig. 4.8.

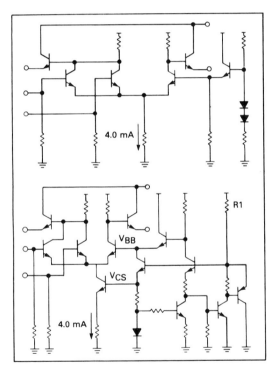

Fig. 4.9 Comparing 10K with 10KH

So far we have considered ECL3 and ECL10K as the two logic families in production. There are two others — both derivatives of 10K and both offering improved speeds.

The 10KH range (10H100 etc.) is a high speed replacement for standard 10K. At present available only from Motorola, this relatively new series offers the same power consumption but twice the speed. An oxide isolated process is used to gain both speed and a reduction in chip size. 10KH uses an improved gate design incorporating a voltage regulator instead of a series of diodes; fig. 4.9 compares the two gate designs.

Fig. 4.10 ECL10KH list of products

Function	Device Type	Function	Device Type
NOR gate		*Parity checker*	
Quad 2-input with strobe	10H100	12-bit parity generator-checker	10H160
Quad 2-input	10H102	*Encoders/decoders*	
Triple 4-3-3 input	10H106	Binary to 1-8 (low)	10H161
Dual 3-input 3-output	10H211	Binary to 1-8 (high)	10H162
OR gate		Dual binary to 1-4 (low)	10H171
Quad 2-input	10H103	Dual binary to 1-4 (high)	10H172
Dual 3-input 3-output	10H210	8-input priority encoder	10H165
AND gates		*Data selector/multiplexer*	
Quad AND	10H104	2-line multiplexer (25 ohm)	10H155
Complex gates		4-line multiplexer (25 ohm)	10H156
Quad OR/NOR	10H101	Quad 2-input multiplexer (noninverting)	10H158
Triple 2-3-2 input OR/NOR	10H105		
Triple exclusive OR/NOR	10H107	Quad 2-input multiplexer (inverting)	10H159
Dual 4-5 input OR/NOR	10H109		
Quad exclusive OR	10H113	8-line multiplexer	10H164
Dual 2-wide OR-AND/OR-AND invert	10H117	Quad 2-input multiplexer/latch	10H173
		Dual 4-1 multiplexer	10H174
Dual 2-wide 3-input OR/AND	10H118	*Counters*	
4-wide 4-3-3-3 input OR-AND	10H119	Universal hexadecimal	10H136
4-wide OR-AND/OR-AND invert	10H121	Binary counter	10H178
Hex buffer w/enable	10H188	*Arithmetic functions*	
Hex inverter w/enable	10H189	Look ahead carry block	10H179
Translators		Dual high speed adder/ subtractor	10H180
Quad TTL to MECL	10H124		
Quad MECL to TTL	10H125	4-bit ALU	10H181
Receivers		*Special function*	
Quad line receiver	10H115	4-bit universal shift register	10H141
Triple line receiver	10H116	16 x 4 bit register file	10H145
Flip-flops/latches		5-bit magnitude comparator	10H166
Dual D master slave flip-flop	10H131	Bidirectional bus driver (25 ohms)	10H199
Dual J-K master slave flip-flop	10H135		
Hex D flip-flop	10H176		
Dual D latch	10H130		
Quint latch	10H175		
Hex D flip-flop w/common reset	10H186A		

Voltage compensation of this type is a standard ECL technique which had previously been avoided in logic family products because of the extra complexity. A current source replaces the emitter resistor and this gives a further improvement. At present it is only possible to obtain 10KH for use from 0 to +75°C (this is a temperature range established for ECL memories) but the change of parameters over this range is far better than had previously been available.

Eventually it is possible that the majority of ECL10K products will be available in a 10KH version; today the range is as shown in fig. 4.10.

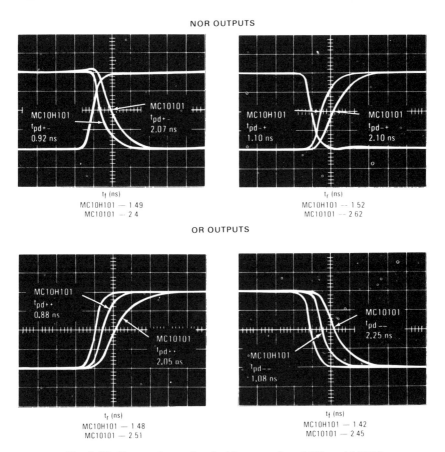

Fig. 4.11 Comparison of switching speeds – 10K and 10KH

The difference in performance between the two ranges can be observed from fig. 4.11. Propagation delays for most products are 1.5 ns rather than 2.9 ns – rise and fall times are 2.0 ns rather than 3.3 ns. Toggle frequencies are doubled to 250 MHz (for the 10H131).

Although ECL10KH products are fairly easy to use – certainly easier than ECL3 – the printed circuit board layout requirements are more severe than for normal 10K. Fortunately it is relatively easy to find out (by substitution) if any changes are needed in a system designed originally for 10K.

The second (but much earlier) high speed version of ECL10K is the 100K series (numbered from 100100 upwards). Introduced by Fairchild and second-sourced by Signetics (Philips) the purpose of the range is to offer true 'subnanosecond' logic (propagation delays below 1 ns) with the complexity of 10K and reasonable ease of use. Despite the similarity of the numbering system it was decided at the outset to package 100K in 24 lead flatpacks; dual-in-line packages were thought to be unsuitable for subnanosecond logic, especially for LSI functions. This meant that functions could be increased in complexity — the 10130 dual latch becoming the 100130 triple latch, for example. Fig. 4.12 gives a listing of the 100K range.

Fig. 4.12 ECL100K list of products (being extended)

Function	Device	Function	Device
Triple 5-input OR/NOR	100101	Quad multiplexer/latch	100155
Quint 2-input OR/NOR	100102	Mask-merge	100156
Quint exclusive OR/NOR	100107	Shift matrix	100158
Quad driver	100112	Dual 9-bit parity	100160
High-speed line driver	100113	Dual 8-input multiplexer	100163
Quad line receiver	100114	16-input multiplexer	100164
Triple 2-wide OA/OAI	100117	Universal priority encoder	100165
5-wide 5, 4, 4, 4, 2 OA/OAI	100118	9-bit comparator	100166
9-bit buffer gate	100122	Universal decoder	100170
Hex bus driver	100123	Triple 4-input multiplexer	100171
TTL-100K ECL translator	100124	Carry lookahead	100179
100K ECL-TTL translator	100125	Fast 6-bit adder	100180
Back plane driver	100126	4-bit binary/BCD ALU	100181
Triple D latch	100130	9-bit wallace tree adder	100182
Triple D flip-flop	100131	2 x 8-bit recode multiplier	100183
Counter/shift register	100136	Quint transceiver	100194
8-bit shift register	100141	Address and data interface unit (ADIU)	100220
4 x 4 content addressable memory	100142	Multi-function network (MFN)	100221
16 x 4 register file	100145	Dual access stack (DAS)	100222
Hex D latch	100150	Program interface unit (PIU)	100223
Hex D flip-flop	100151	Microprogram sequencer (MPS)	100224

An opportunity was taken at the same time to increase the stability of the voltage levels by including a voltage regulator on the chip. Both temperature and supply voltage compensation are included, with the result that operation can be assured over a wide supply voltage range from -4.2 V to -5.7 V. Even over a temperature range from -30 to $+85°$C there is almost no change in logic levels.

The disadvantage of this improvement is that ECL10K and

ECL100K are incompatible. The faster edge speeds make it difficult to mix the two products anyway, so ECL100K designs cannot readily be derived from or used to improve an existing 10K design.

The diagram of fig. 4.13 shows a typical gate circuit.

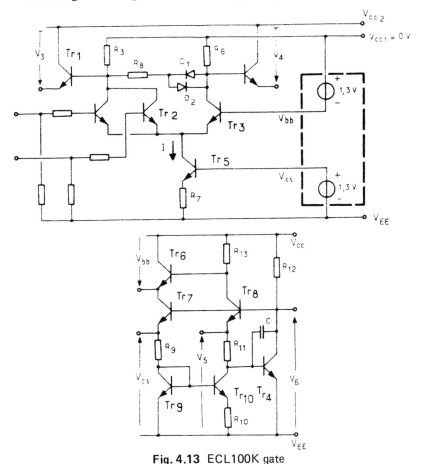

Fig. 4.13 ECL100K gate

Since 1979 it has been possible to buy 100K in a narrow 24 lead dual-in-line package and this has improved the popularity of the series. The range of products now available is almost as impressive as the 10K series, with both 4 bit and 8 bit ALU processor kits extending the capability. The 10K series remains more popular, however, and the high speed market seems to be moving towards semicustom logic arrays (which tend to be 10K compatible anyway).

Memories using ECL technology are usually 10K compatible.

Read only memories (PROMs) and read/write memories (RAMs) are both in production, being sold generally as stand-alone items rather than along with other 10K products. The temperature range is normally narrower, too, operation being guaranteed only from 0 to +75°C for commercial grade although the full military range can be obtained in some cases. A list of ECL memories on the market is given in fig. 4.14.

Fig. 4.14 ECL memory products

RAM (Read/Write)		
Device	Organisation	Access Time
10143	8 x 2	15
10144	256 x 1	26
10145	16 x 4	15
10H145	16 x 4	6
10146	1024 x 1	29
10147	128 x 1	15
10148	64 x 1	15
10152	256 x 1	15
10405	128 x 1	15
10410	256 x 1	26
10415	1024 x 1	29
10422	256 x 4	15
10470	4096 x 1	35
10474	1024 x 4	25
10544	256 x 1	26
10545	16 x 4	15
10546	1024 x 1	29
10547	128 x 1	15
10548	64 x 1	15
10552	256 x 1	15
100402	16 x 4	5
100414	256 x 1	10
100415	1024 x 1	20
100422	256 x 4	10
100470	4096 x 1	35
100474	1024 x 4	35

ROM (Read Only)		
Device	Organisation	Access Time
10139	32 x 8	20
10149	256 x 4	25
10539	32 x 8	20
10549	256 x 4	25
100416	256 x 4	20

An example of an ECL RAM is the 10146 (similar to the 10415). This is a 1024 x 1 read/write memory operating from a single −5.2 V supply. A block diagram appears in fig. 4.15.

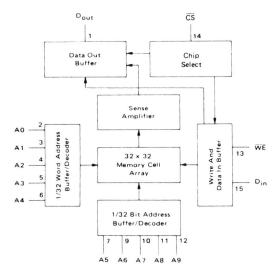

TRUTH TABLE

MODE	INPUT			OUTPUT
	$\overline{CS}$	$\overline{WE}$	D_{in}	D_{out}
Write "0"	L	L	L	L
Write "1"	L	L	H	L
Read	L	H	ϕ	Q
Disabled	H	ϕ	ϕ	L

ϕ = Don't Care

Fig. 4.15 The 10146 ECL1K RAM

There are ten address inputs (A0 ... A9) which identify the individual memory cell. A 'write enable' input (WE) determines whether or not the RAM is in the READ or WRITE mode. The data input and output pins are gated by a 'chip select' pin which identifies this memory from others in an array of similar memories.

In the READ mode it takes 29 ns (max) between the correct address input being applied to A0 ... A9 and the output data appearing. This 'address access time' is shown as t_{AA} in fig. 4.16.

In the WRITE mode the correct address must be supplied before the data is read at the input. Then after a further wait the write enable pin must be lowered to 0. After a minimum wait of 25 ns (t_W) this pin is returned to 1 and a further 2 ns must elapse before the address is removed. Fig. 4.16 illustrates the timing

CHIP SELECT ACCESS TIME

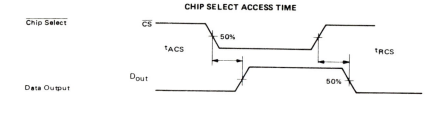

ADDRESS ACCESS TIME

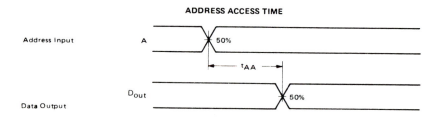

WRITE STROBE MODE

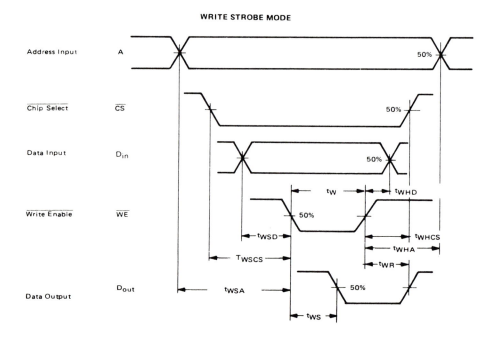

Fig. 4.16 Timing diagram of the 10146 RAM

diagram; note how the chip select input further complicates the situation. Detailed memory system design requires considerable expertise.

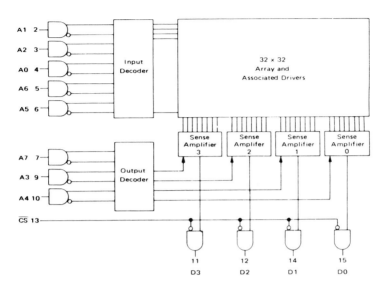

Fig. 4.17 10149 1K PROM

The 10149 is a 1024 bit PROM organised as 256 words, each of 4 bits. Fig. 4.17 shows the arrangement. Eight address pins (A0 . . . A7) identify an individual cell; a 'chip select' pin gates the four data outputs and an extra pin is used for programming purposes.

No ROMs (factory programmed) using ECL technology are available on the open market yet, although it is possible that custom products are being manufactured. PROMs require individual cell programming; each bit is set to 1 unless changed by 'fusing' the appropriate bit. This is done by using a special PROM programmer which addresses the required cell and then applies a short +12 V pulse on the programming pin to 'blow the fuse'. The details of the circuitry needed to do this are readily available and will not be mentioned here.

Thereafter the PROM behaves as a normal ROM (it cannot be reprogrammed) with timing arrangements similar to a RAM in the READ mode. The address access time is 25 ns max and it takes another 10 ns to select the chip if required.

More information on ECL memories can be obtained in literature produced by Motorola, Fairchild, Signetics (Philips) and other manufacturers.

CHAPTER 5

High speed dividers

High speed divider technology has moved a long way from the first RTL flip-flops which could divide their input frequency by two and operate at input frequencies of a few MHz. Now it is possible to buy a fully specified ECL divider to operate at 2000 MHz. Nor is the division ratio restricted to 2 or 4; you can obtain almost any worthwhile ratio up to 256 and beyond. There are dual ratio 'two modulus' and even 'four modulus' dividers which can be used as prescalers, or, as shown in chapter 6, as part of a multi-channel frequency synthesiser. Multiple output binary counters are also manufactured.

Many people associate ECL with high current consumption. While this may be true with logic circuits which are required to drive 50 Ω lines the output stages of many ECL dividers operate at relatively low frequencies and are often designed to be compatible with TTL. A standard 150 MHz divide by 10 circuit in ECL will typically consume only 10 mA from a TTL type 5 V supply (and cost less than a high current Schottky TTL divider operating at half that frequency).

The normal application of a prescaler (fixed ratio divider) is the reduction of a signal from a high frequency to one at which precise frequency measurement or comparison can be carried out. A common example is to be found in car radio/cassette players or domestic hi-fi systems when the frequency of an integral radio tuner is shown on a four digit display. Contrary to popular belief this is not achieved by connecting a tuning potentiometer to a digital voltmeter; it is in fact a genuine frequency counter connected to the local oscillator. Since the counter/display circuit is fairly complex (it also incorporates an offset to allow for the IF of the radio) it is invariably implemented in MOS technology with a maximum input frequency of a few MHz. The local oscillator will, at the top end of VHF Band 2, have worst case frequency of

120 MHz (108 + 10.7) and clearly there is a need for a divider to prescale this input. Fig. 5.1 illustrates the concept.

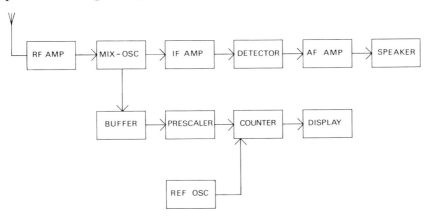

Fig. 5.1 Application of a prescaler in frequency display radio

Many prescaling factors (division ratios) are used but divide by 10, divide by 20 and divide by 100 are most common. The most popular circuit is the '8629' which divides by 100 and has a TTL type output. It is easy to use as the applications circuit of fig. 5.2 shows.

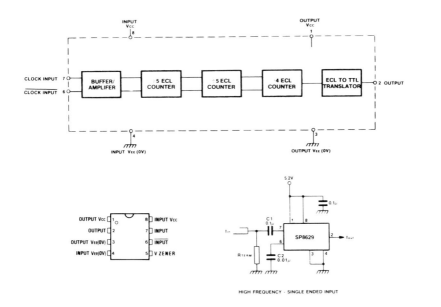

Fig. 5.2 SP8629 prescaler

An input of about 100 mV peak-peak is needed and the output is TTL or CMOS compatible. This particular circuit is an interesting example of the ability of ECL to out-perform Schottky TTL in that it is possible to buy a Schottky TTL version of the 8629 from National Semiconductors. The ECL version (Plessey) is more sensitive and takes less current.

This example serves to illustrate that high speed dividers and counters have some interesting applications, that they need not be expensive and that they are generally not difficult to use. It is now worth looking at the internal configuration of the simplest of these circuits — the fixed ratio divider or prescaler.

Prescalers originate from flip-flops. The ECL3 MC/SP1690 was for years the cheapest 1 GHz divide by 4 function (albeit not the most reliable!). Most high speed dividers and counters on the market are designed around a combination of flip-flops which, with feedback, allow almost any division ratio. The flip-flop itself is normally edge triggered (usually on the positive going input edge) and thus requires a reasonably sharp edged input waveform of at least some tens of volts per microsecond. A D type flip-flop is illustrated in fig. 5.3.

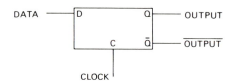

CLOCK INPUT	PREVIOUS DATA INPUT	OUTPUT
1 ⌐ 0	0	0
1 ⌐ 0	1	1
1 ⌐ 0	0 OR 1	NO CHANGE

Fig. 5.3 D type flip-flop

The operation of a D type flip-flop is in two stages. The logic level present on the D input when the clock input C goes from 1 to 0 (negative) is transferred internally to a master flip-flop. The output remains unchanged. Then when the clock input C rises from 0 to 1 (positive) the data in the master flip-flop is transferred to a slave flip-flop which controls the output Q. There is normally also an inverting output $\overline{Q}$ which is always at 1 when Q is at 0 and vice versa. Within an integrated circuit there are also $\overline{D}$ and $\overline{C}$ inputs but there is no need to consider these now as they do not affect the principles of operation.

A flip-flop by itself is not a divider. It simply transfers the logic level on the D input to the Q output after a delay determined by the clock input. But if the $\overline{Q}$ output is connected to D then the logic level on the D input will always be opposite to that of the Q output. Then every time the clock input C changes from 0 to 1 the Q output will change polarity. It is, in fact, a divide by 2 circuit with C as the input and Q as the output. Fig. 5.4 shows the configuration and timing diagram.

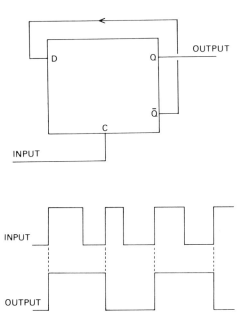

Fig. 5.4 Divide by 2 circuit

At this stage it is worth while to look at the circuit diagram of a divide by 2 prescaler. Fig. 5.5 shows the Plessey SP8602, a 500 MHz prescaler which consumes 12 mA from a 5 V supply. The SP8602 consists of a master flip-flop, a slave flip-flop and an output buffer. The inputs (pins 1 and 2) are provided with bias from a four diode regulator and the bias point is externally decoupled by a capacitor at pin 3. The input signal is coupled into pin 1 through a small capacitor; the other input is normally decoupled unless a 'push-pull' input is available.

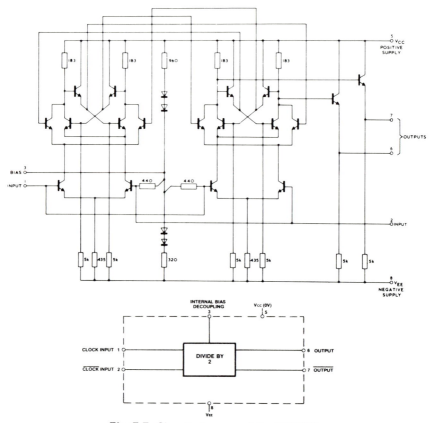

Fig. 5.5 Circuit diagram of the SP8602

Not all prescalers divide by two. It is clearly possible to connect several in cascade to produce total division ratios of 4, 8, 16, and so on. A prescaler with two or more stages can be either synchronous (if each D flip-flop stage is clocked from the input) or asynchronous (if each stage is clocked from the output of the previous stage). An asynchronous prescaler is sometimes called a 'ripple through counter' for obvious reasons and most prescalers with four or more stages are of this type. The difference between the two is shown in fig. 5.6.

It is difficult to draw the timing diagram of any synchronous counter because of the effect of the feedback so a simple truth table is normally drawn up. Each Q output is identified separately

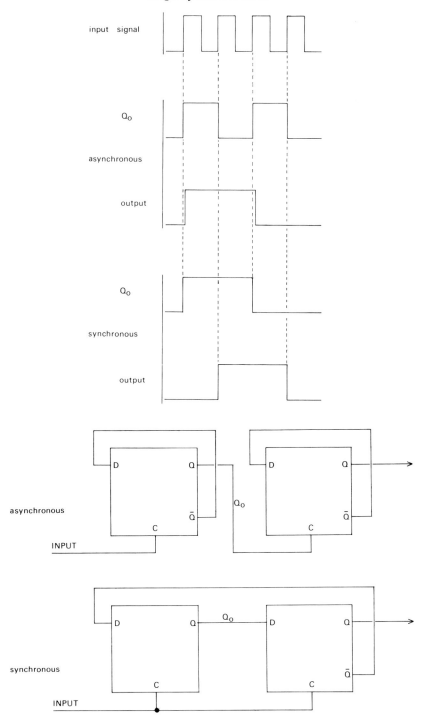

Fig. 5.6 Comparison between asynchronous and synchronous prescalers

and the table shows every possible combination of the output levels 'before' and 'after' a positive clock input transition. Not every combination of output levels may be possible when normal operation takes place but unless special design precautions have been taken it is possible for an otherwise incorrect combination to exist when the prescaler is initially switched on. It is important that the prescaler is able to move out of the incorrect combination after a minimum number of clocking cycles and that is why the truth table should show every possible combination. The truth table for the synchronous divide by 4 prescaler is shown in fig. 5.7.

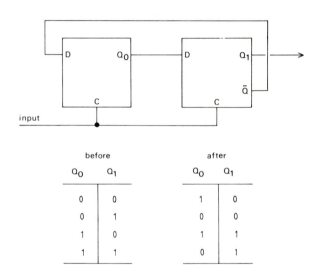

Fig. 5.7 Truth table for divide by 4 synchronous prescaler

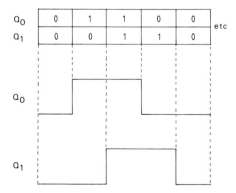

Fig. 5.8 Generation of timing diagram

This table can be explained as follows. When both Q_0 and Q_1 are at 0 the $\bar{Q}$ output (at 1) is fed back to the input of the first stage. So the D inputs are 1 (first stage) and 0 (second stage) causing the outputs to change to $Q_0 = 1$, $Q_1 = 0$ after clocking. The other combinations can easily be verified.

Now the timing diagram can be constructed. Assume a starting stage of $Q_0 = 0$, $Q_1 = 0$. This changes to 1, 0 after clocking. By looking at 1, 0 in the 'before' table it can be seen that the next stage will be 1, 1. This process can be continued as shown in fig. 5.8. In this figure each vertical line corresponds to a positive going input signal.

Until now we have only considered a two stage (divide by 4) arrangement although this is extendable to higher powers of two. By applying feedback around this type of divider it is possible to reduce the count — from 4 to 3, for example. This technique is applicable to synchronous or asynchronous counters but it happens that most commercially available prescalers which divide by prime numbers (3, 5, 7 and so on) are synchronous. Almost all binary ratios other than 2 or 4 are constructed asynchronously.

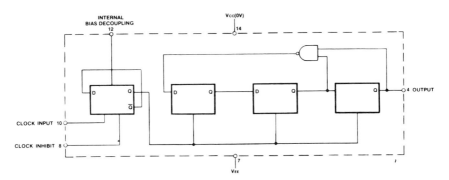

Fig. 5.9 Divide by 10 configuration

A commonly used division ratio is 10. The usual arrangement is a simple D flip-flop followed by a synchronous divide by 5. Fig. 5.9 shows a typical circuit. The divide by 5 section consists of the three flip-flops in the centre of the diagram together with the OR gate. If the Q outputs of these flip-flops are labelled Q1, Q2 and Q3 then a truth table can be drawn up as shown in fig. 5.10.

The three 'before' states marked with an asterisk can only arise during start-up conditions. Since they do not appear in the 'after' states they cannot be the result of a normal counting sequence. There is a 3 in 8 chance that the prescaler will start in one of these states but it only takes one or two clock periods for correct counting to commence. A timing diagram appears in fig. 5.11.

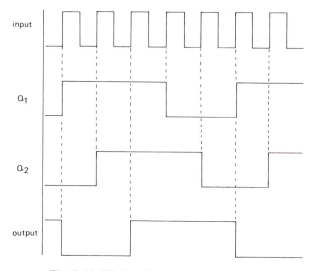

	before					after		
	Q_1	Q_2	Q_3			Q_1	Q_2	Q_3
*	0	0	0			1	0	0
	0	0	1			1	0	0
*	0	1	0			1	0	1
	0	1	1			0	0	1
	1	0	0			1	1	0
*	1	0	1			1	1	0
	1	1	0			1	1	1
	1	1	1			0	1	1

Fig. 5.10 Truth table for divide by 5

Fig. 5.11 Timing diagram for divide by 5

A point worth noting from this diagram is that the output mark-space ratio is 3:2 rather than the normal 1:1. This will normally have no effect on the following stages but may be important in some applications. Mark-space ratios are not always quoted in data sheets but can normally be calculated (or measured).

The divide by 10 prescaler just examined includes most of the features likely to be encountered. A point often questioned by designers familiar with TTL or CMOS counter design is the lack of a reset input to the flip-flop stages. Some ECL counters have reset inputs (although some really act as inhibit inputs) but in general the time taken to reset each stage is in tens of nanoseconds, too long to allow the use of reset inputs as part of the feedback network in a high speed counter.

Divider data sheets do not benefit from the standardisation of being part of an established logic family. It is difficult to choose the best product for an application when confronted with a pile of data sheets of possible products from several manufacturers. Not all data sheets specify all parameters of general interest. A TV synthesis prescaler will not often have a guaranteed propagation delay, for example. But since this is a parameter which is determined primarily by design it may be possible to deduce the normal spread and so avoid having to pay more for a tested product. There follows a number of features which appear in data sheets of ECL counters and dividers.

Package

High speed dividers tend to be manufactured in both plastic and hermetic packages. Avoid plastic packages where continuous operation at temperatures above 85°C is expected or where there is a high level of moisture.

Operating temperature

It is a characteristic of ECL that voltage levels vary with temperature. Few manufacturers are prepared to guarantee operation more than 50°C away from the temperature at which testing takes place, and a commercial temperature range of −30 to +70°C (sometimes 0 to +70) has become popular. The manufacturer will test these products 100% at 20°C and a sample from each batch at temperature extremes. The frequency performance of many dividers tends to fall dramatically as temperature rises and this means that expensive temperature testing is needed. Most military grade products carry a surcharge of 50% or more.

Dividers which operate at 1 GHz and above require fairly high supply currents, often leading to a package dissipation of 500 mW. In these cases it is important to establish whether or not heatsinking is needed to reduce the thermal resistance between package and ambient. Some manufacturers specify a case (package) temperature rather than ambient for this reason. Fig. 5.12 shows how to calculate chip and case temperatures.

Thermal resistance figures between junction and case depend on the package and bonding technique and cannot be improved. But the case to ambient resistance can normally be halved with even a small heatsink. Some typical figures are shown in table 5.1.

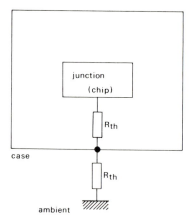

Fig. 5.12 Calculating temperatures

Table 5.1 Thermal resistance figures
Thermal Resistance (in still air)

Package	J-A	J-C
8 lead plastic	200	
14 lead plastic	165	
16 lead plastic	160	
8 lead ceramic	150	40
14 lead ceramic	110	30
16 lead ceramic	110	30
8 lead metal	210	60

Junction (chip) temperature

In the case of a 14 lead ceramic package a typical junction to ambient thermal resistance is $110°C/W$. If 500 mW is dissipated in the IC then the rise in junction temperature will be half of 110, i.e. $55°C$. If the maximum junction temperature is $150°C$ then the divider can operate up to $95°C$ ambient $(95 + 110/2 = 150)$.

Case temperature

The calculation of case temperature is useful because it can be measured and compared with the theory to give an indication of the accuracy of the heatsinking arrangements.

Taking the example above, if the junction to case thermal

resistance is 30°C/W this leaves 80°C/W for case to ambient. The total temperature rise across this resistance is 55°C so the rise across the case to ambient part is 80/110ths of this: 40°C. The case temperature is therefore 40°C above ambient, i.e. 135°C.

It is always wise to stay well inside maximum temperature ratings and a heatsink should be used in cases of doubt. One final point on the subject of operating temperature. Some manufacturers state 'suitable for operation from 0°C to +70°C' or something similar, but only guarantee operation at 25°C. This means that although all products will operate at +70°C, it does not follow that they will fully meet the specification. Some allowance should be made for this; perhaps a 10% reduction in the maximum operating frequency. Manufacturers who guarantee a certain maximum frequency over a temperature range have already made this allowance.

Supply voltage

Dividers are normally specified for operation either from ECL supplies (−5.2 V) or TTL (+5.0 V) to suit the system in which they would normally be used. A 1 GHz divide by 2 circuit with 500 MHz ECL outputs would not be expected to operate from TTL supplies, for example. The distinction between negative and positive supply voltages indicates only that the positive and negative supply pins (respectively) are connected to earth. There is no difference within the integrated circuit and it is almost always possible to earth the 'wrong' supply side instead; this converts a −5.2 V product to +5.2 V. Occasionally, a non-standard supply voltage, normally 6.8 V, is specified. This can be regulated either by a zener diode regulator or an integrated circuit.

A data sheet will specify the range of supply voltages over which performance is guaranteed. Distinguish carefully between, for example, 5 V and 5 V ± 0.25 V. It is possible that a divider specified only for operation at 5 V may fail to operate reliably at +4.75 V, especially at low temperatures.

Input signal

ECL circuits normally require input voltage swings of about 1 V peak-peak. Dividers are normally a little more sensitive and are specified for operation over a range of input voltages (400 mV to 800 mV peak-peak, for example) to avoid the need to adjust input levels to exact values. The signal source, often a limiting type preamplifier, must provide a suitable input voltage to the divider input impedance. The equivalent input circuit of dividers is similar to that shown in fig. 5.13. Note that some dividers, especially those intended for use in radio and TV applications, have a different type of input stage incorporating a preamplifier.

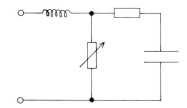

Fig. 5.13 Equivalent input impedance

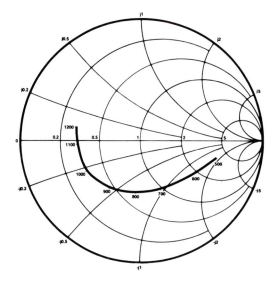

Fig. 5.14 Input impedance chart

Up to 50 MHz the input is mainly resistive but at higher frequencies the capacitance begins to dominate. At still higher frequencies the input resistance falls due to transistor frequency limitations (reduction of beta). Above 400 MHz the parasitic inductance of lead wires has an increasing effect and results become more dependent on the circuit board layout and input coupling capacitors. Manufacturers normally publish complex impedance charts of each divider type and fig. 5.14 shows a typical example. This type of chart, sometimes known as a Smith chart, is based on two sets of circles — constant resistance and constant reactance. Fig. 5.15 illustrates these.

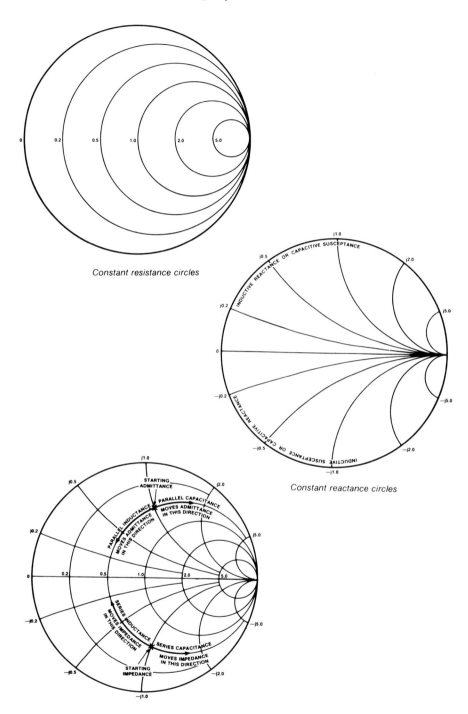

Constant resistance circles

Constant reactance circles

Fig. 5.15 Simplified impedance chart

A point is plotted on the chart in the following manner. The input resistance (ignoring C and L effects) tends to fall with frequency due partly to the gain reduction of the input transistors. At a given frequency the value can be plotted on a circle. In the case of the divider of fig. 5.14, at 700 MHz the line crosses the constant resistance circle marked '1' (indicating 50 Ω since this chart is 'normalised' to that value). At 900 MHz the resistance has fallen to 25 Ω. Ultimately the resistance appears to fall to about 15 Ω at the highest frequencies.

If there were no contribution from inductance and capacitance the impedance chart would be a straight horizontal line through the middle of the chart. When these effects are added, however, they have the effect of moving the point around the circle of constant resistance. When the effect is of shunt capacitance or series inductance, for example, the imaginary component becomes more positive and the point moves clockwise. This effect can be seen clearly in fig. 5.14. As the frequency increases so these effects become more prominent. At 900 MHz the impedance is $(25\text{-j}25)$ Ω.

Smith charts allow graphical calculation of compensating networks so that the output of a preamplifier can match the input of the divider. A lot of mathematics can be avoided. Most reference books include a section on impedance charts and a number of books cover the subject in great detail.

Although a maximum and minimum guaranteed input signal voltage is specified, it may be useful to know what happens outside these levels so that the preamplifier frequency response can be designed to give the widest safety margin. There are three features of a typical input sensitivity graph:

(a) At low and high frequency extremes the sensitivity falls off.
(b) At some intermediate frequency the sensitivity improves dramatically. When no input signal is present there is a risk of self oscillation at this frequency.
(c) At some intermediate frequency there is a risk of 'blocking' at high input levels. The divider ceases to count under these conditions.

Fig. 5.16 shows a typical input sensitivity graph.
It is possible to improve this performance in two areas:

(a) extension of the low frequency performance;
(b) removal of self-oscillation risk.

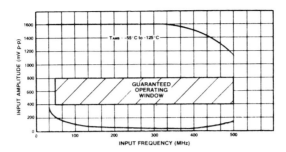

Fig. 5.16 Typical input sensitivity

First it is necessary to look at why these limitations occur. We saw earlier that the operation of a D type flip-flop involves the transfer of data from master to slave as the clock input rises from 0 to 1. We assumed then that all the appropriate transistors changed state instantaneously with the clock input. This is a realistic assumption when the clock edge is fast, but a situation could clearly arise with a slower clock input when only part of the transition has taken place and an 'incorrect' logic state exists for a few nanoseconds. A phenomenon known as charge storage will normally ensure that there is no loss of data during a short period but clock rise and fall times of more than a few nanoseconds will cause miscounting to take place. Provided a square wave input is provided, then operation can continue as normal down to DC.

Manufacturers' data sheets normally specify a minimum input slew rate of 50 V/μs or so; the slew rate of any particular waveform can be calculated from the derivative of the function or by measurement. The most common example is of a sine wave input:

$$V = V_0 \sin \omega t$$
$$\frac{dv}{dt} = \omega V_0 \cos \omega t$$
$$\therefore \max \frac{dv}{dt} = \omega V_0$$
$$= \pi f \text{ x peak to peak voltage}$$

So a 500 V/μs slew rate corresponds to a 25 MHz sine wave with peak-peak amplitude of 640 mV. Operation at frequencies less than this is still possible, but the input signal must be 'squared up' to provide a suitable edge.

Some dividers are specially designed to operate down to low frequencies either by adding hysteresis (which converts edge triggering to level triggering but can allow jitter to take place) or by allowing direct coupling to the input with externally applied bias. Although most early prescalers were designed to be directly coupled for compatibility with existing logic families (ECL2), the inclusion of bias networks on chip allows an increase in sensitivity with a saving in external components.

The use of internal biasing is also partly responsible for the second problem, that of self-oscillation when no input is present. If no solution is provided on the data sheet, then a resistor of a few kilohms in value should be connected between the input pin and the negative supply pin (V_{EE}). This has the effect of biasing the clock input in one direction which reduces the sensitivity as well as curing the problem. The resistor value should be chosen to be as high as possible.

Timing measurements

Propagation delay, measured from a point on the positive edge of the clock input to the corresponding point on the positive edge of the output, is illustrated in fig. 5.17. This 'clock to output' delay is almost independent of input frequency and, in a synchronous counter, is fairly small — a few nanoseconds, corresponding to the delay of a single stage. Asynchronous counters normally have longer delays because of the contribution from each stage. This is the only timing measurement normally specified on a prescaler because it can reliably be guaranteed by design. Output rise and fall times are normally insignificant unless an open collector output is provided. Counters normally have a number of additional tests including the time delay between a specified reset pulse and the transition of all outputs to zero.

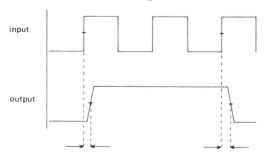

Fig. 5.17 Propagation delays

Output stages

Dividers normally have emitter follower (ECL) or open collector (TTL/CMOS) outputs, although low frequency ECL output stages are occasionally designed in a different way. Although emitter follower outputs are normal for all ECL circuits, there may not be enough drive current for a 50 Ω transmission line with all types of dividers.

Open collector outputs are suitable up to 30 MHz or so but suffer from the problem of slow rise-time. Fig. 5.18 illustrates the problem.

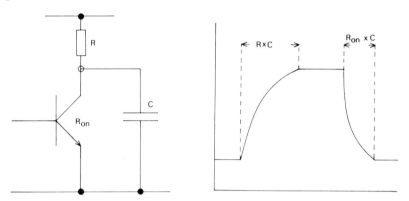

Fig. 5.18 Open collector output stage. Since R_{ON} is much smaller than R_L, the negative going edge (1 to 0) is much sharper.

When there is no active pull-up, the load capacitance must charge up through a load resistor. Assuming typical values of 3 pF and 5 kΩ, the time constant is 15 ns and the 10% to 90% rise time probably 20 ns or more. Because of this there is a tendency to include an internal active load on circuits which can support the increased supply current requirement. The open collector output allows easier interfacing to CMOS as it can be 'pulled up' (the load resistor connected to a higher CMOS supply voltage).

Choosing a high speed divider for a particular application is simplified by the relatively small number of manufacturers and by the natural subdivision of products into market areas. Dividers can be grouped into one of three categories:

  (i) fixed ratio (prescalers),
  (ii) counters (with more than one output),
  (iii) 2, 3 or 4 modulus dividers.

The third category is intended for use in frequency synthesisers and the products will be discussed separately.

Many prescalers are used for measurement or frequency comparison but the vast majority are sold for frequency synthesis in television receivers. TV prescalers normally divide by 64 or 256 (not particularly convenient choices), and although usually very sensitive, their current consumption is high. Low cost volume production of a 950 MHz TV divider obviously involves a number of compromises and the non-TV user should read the data sheets carefully. It should not be assumed that input sensitivity is constant over the whole frequency and temperature range, for example. Remember that if a TV manufacturer can buy one million pieces for one dollar each, it does not follow that a smaller user will be given the benefit of a low price.

A further problem is that supply and demand is controlled by the consumer industry. When a design becomes outmoded, like the early 6.8 V supply voltage TV dividers, it ceases to be produced.

The second main market is in frequency display for VHF radio. Division ratios of 10, 20, and 100 are normal depending on the type of frequency display circuit being used, and the number of frequency bands being covered. The circuits are usually 8 lead dual-in-line plastic devices, but occasionally single-in-line packages are produced. Once again the user should check data sheets carefully and ensure that the device he plans to use will operate over the temperature and frequency range he requires.

The non-consumer area can be split into two: measuring and test equipment, and professional radio synthesisers. Professional radio synthesisers are covered in detail in the next chapter, but occasionally divide by 2 or divide by 4 prescalers are used to extend the frequency range offered by the basic synthesiser to higher frequency bands.

The requirement of the measuring and test equipment market is extremely varied. Nuclear particle detectors, oscilloscope time bases, signal generators and frequency counters can all use high speed dividers, either in a direct frequency counting application up to 700 MHz or for prescaling up to 2 GHz.

Fixed ratio prescalers tend to fall into the following categories:

150 MHz plastic (for radio)
    div 10
    div 20
    div 100
    TTL/CMOS outputs

200 MHz metal can (military)
 div 2 to div 32
 low current
 TTL/CMOS outputs

600 MHz (max) medium cost
 many ratios
 many packages
 TTL or ECL outputs

1 GHz plastic (for TV)
 div 64
 div 256
 TTL or ECL outputs

2 GHz (max)
 div 2
 div 4 (most popular)
 div 8
 div 10 (1.5 GHz max)
 ceramic package
 ECL outputs

The SP8629 has already been described as a typical low cost prescaler of the first category; an example of a low power military divider is the Plessey SP8659 shown in fig. 5.19.

A typical feature of this type of product is the open collector output which saves current and makes interfacing easy. Propagation delays are not important in the application; they are relatively high because of the asynchronous design and the output stage. Operation is guaranteed from −55 to +125°C and using them is fairly straightforward.

Prescalers intended for more general use up to about 600 MHz tend to have a current consumption of around 50 mA or more. At these frequencies it becomes necessary to introduce ECL output stages, especially with low division ratios. At frequencies above 1 GHz the ECL output becomes essential. The present frequency limit of dividers on the open market is 2 GHz (for a division ratio of 4) but there have been demonstrations of frequencies well above this in research laboratories. The ultimate limit in silicon is hard to define, but must surely exceed 5 GHz eventually (if there is a market!). A typical example of a 1.5 GHz prescaler is the Plessey SP8611 shown in fig. 5.20.

The SP8611 is a selection of the SP8610 1 GHz divider; the

basic chip is assembled and final testing determines which will make the SP8611 category. Above 70°C the frequency performance deteriorates so that at +125°C (case temperature, not ambient) operation is only guaranteed to 1.3 GHz. The current consumption is 100 mA — typical for this type of design although improvements in processing now allow substantial reductions. Both Fairchild and Signetics (Philips) produce dividers interchangeable with the SP8610/11.

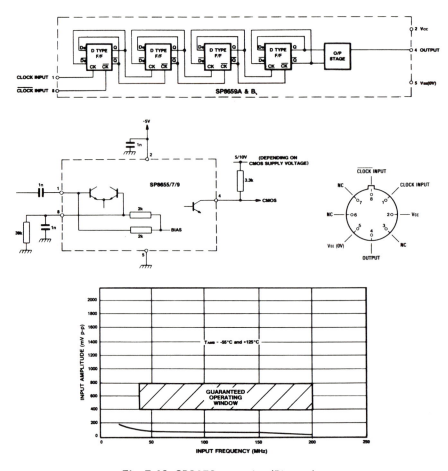

Fig. 5.19 SP8659 prescaler (Plessey).

Prescalers for television are of a basically similar design but intended only for use up to 950 MHz (up to 1.3 GHz in some cable TV systems). The division ratios are either 64 or 256 and current consumption is generally lower than for corresponding

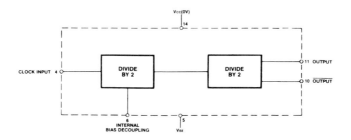

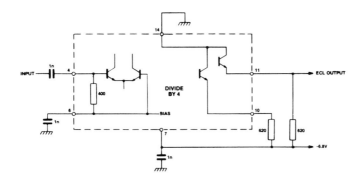

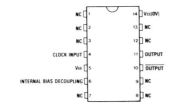

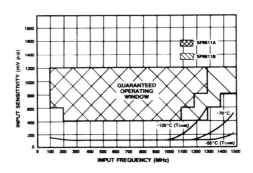

Fig. 5.20 SP8611 prescaler (Plessey)

professional products. Designs seem to change fairly rapidly as fashions change but most include a pre-amplifier on the chip to give an improvement in sensitivity. An example of a really low current product is the Plessey SP4632, a 1 GHz divide by 64 which only takes 25 mA (typ) and has a sensitivity guarantee of 17.5 mV RMS (see fig. 5.21).

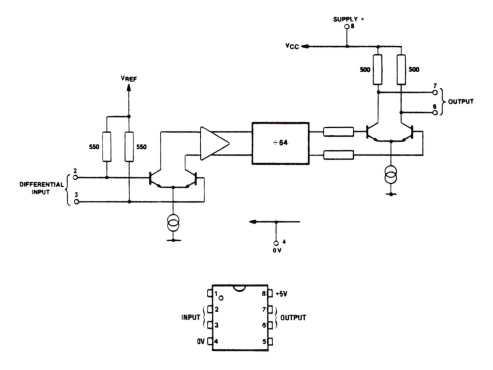

Fig. 5.21 SP4632 TV prescaler (Plessey)

The SP4632 features an unusual collector driven ECL output circuit which is adequate for the relatively low output frequency. The output impedance is approximately 500 Ω, unsuitable for 50 Ω applications but ideal for the requirement in a TV synthesiser.

The counter market is relatively small and an example of a typical product is shown in fig. 5.22.

The Plessey SP8634 is a relatively complicated design with outputs at div 2, div 4, div 8, and div 10 (marked A, B, C and D). It is fully synchronous and has an input which resets all stages to a zero count. There is also a clock inhibit input. The 'carry' output allows several counters to be cascaded in the normal way. The

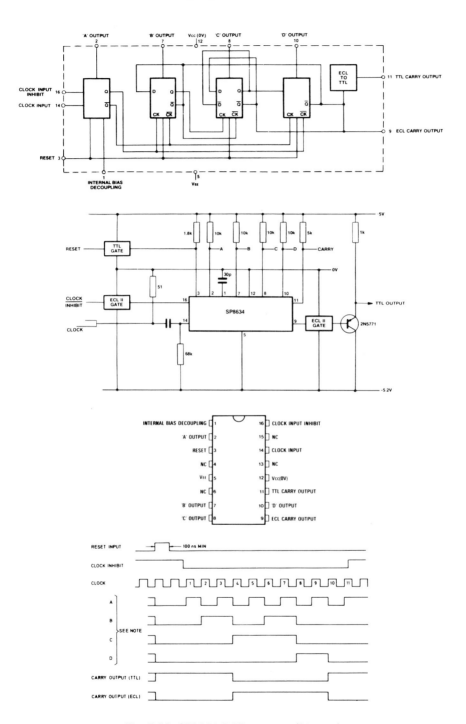

Fig. 5.22 SP8634 BCD counter (Plessey)

design of a complete frequency counter which actually counts every pulse (instead of prescaling the input frequency) is still not an easy task.

Some two modulus dividers are used as prescalers but these products are described in the next chapter. A complete list of all the dividers on the market would take several pages. Many new products are being introduced and it is best to find out from the manufacturers what is recommended for your particular requirement. There follows a list of the most widely known manufacturers and their product ranges:

Fairchild
    11C00 series (e.g. 11C90)
    This series includes many other products

Motorola
    MC1697, 1699 (ECL3 derived)
    MC12000 series (not all dividers)
    MC12500 series (military grade)

Plessey
    SP4000 series (TV)
    SP8000 series (professional)
    Over 100 different dividers

Siemens
    Mainly TV prescalers

Signetics (Philips)
    SAF1000 series (not all dividers)
    Also TV and radio prescalers

Telefunken
    Mainly TV prescalers

There are a number of Japanese products, notably from Toshiba and OKI, but these are not widely sold in Europe.

CHAPTER 6
Frequency synthesis

Although the first fully synthesised military manpack radio (which uses RTL dividers) is still in production there have been so many developments in single and multi-modulus ECL dividers in the last three or four years that even the humblest radio receiver is likely to be affected soon. Most people accept that television tuners, for example, need only a few varicap diodes and preset resistors to store the requisite number of channels. The tuner frequencies of almost 1 GHz and obvious low cost requirement would seem to preclude any possibility of further integration. Yet already by 1980, several million TV receivers contained fully synthesised direct channel tuning systems based on a new generation of low cost ECL prescalers and the appropriate MOS memory and divider control circuitry. These synthesised tuners are apparently cheaper than comparable non-synthesised designs and offer considerable technical advantages. Meanwhile the professional radio market is rapidly moving to a situation where every two or three channel system is fully synthesised. New ultra low power ECL dividers for portable radio applications operating at over 500 MHz actually consume less current than the CMOS circuitry which controls them.

A simple frequency synthesiser is shown in fig. 6.1. A voltage controlled oscillator (VCO) generates an output of approximately the required frequency. This frequency is divided (using an ECL prescaler) and compared with that of a crystal oscillator of known accuracy. The comparator provides a control voltage which alters the VCO frequency and phase until it is exactly 'in lock' with the crystal. The time taken to lock depends largely on the time constants of the filter and is normally under 100 ms. If the division ratio is N and crystal oscillator frequency is f_R then the output frequency is Nxf_R.

The advantage of a phase locked synthesiser is that it is possible to generate frequencies into the GHz region with the accuracy of a quartz crystal operating at, say, 5 MHz. The VCO need only have short term frequency stability.

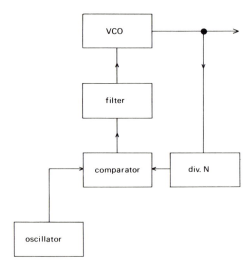

Fig. 6.1 Simple frequency synthesiser

Many applications of synthesisers in radio equipment rely on a second feature – the ease of changing frequency in precise steps. Reference to fig. 6.2 shows how, by changing the division ratio, the output frequency changes in steps of the crystal oscillator frequency.

Fig. 6.2 Changing frequency in a synthesiser

Crystal Oscillator	N	Output Frequency
5 MHz	100	500 MHz
.	99	495 MHz
.	98	490 MHz
.	97	485 MHz
.	.	.
.	.	.
.	.	.
f_R	N	$N \times f_R$

By changing N from 1 to 100 the range of frequencies from 5 MHz to 500 MHz can be covered in steps of 5 MHz provided, of course, that the VCO can cover this range. A more typical requirement is that of VHF mobile radios which are allocated frequencies on a 25 kHz channel spacing. Clearly an extra CMOS divider will be needed to reduce the crystal oscillator frequency to 25 kHz and the value of N will have to be raised accordingly. To cover 450 MHz to 500 MHz in 25 kHz steps will require N to change from 18 000 to 20 000 in steps of 1. This presents quite a problem because no such variable prescalers are available to operate at such high frequencies, even in ECL technology.

A better synthesiser

The solution is simple, although difficult to appreciate at first. If the divide by N prescaler in fig. 6.1 is replaced by a two modulus divider, then it is clear that a choice of two output frequencies is possible. A two modulus divider allows a change in division ratio from, say, 10 to 11 by means of a change in logic level applied to the modulus control input. The most popular division ratios are divide by 40/41, divide by 10/11 and divide by 80/81 (in that order) but many others are available. Each can be set to divide by either of the two ratios and for this reason it is common to consider the use of a popular divide by 10/11 circuit such as Fairchild's 11C90 for a divide by 10 function rather than a simple prescaler.

But when a divide by 10/11 two modulus divider in a synthesiser is controlled in such a way that the division ratio is continuously switched it is possible to imagine that it will effectively divide by a number of intermediate ratios between 10 and 11. There are several methods of achieving this but the simplest is shown in fig. 6.3.

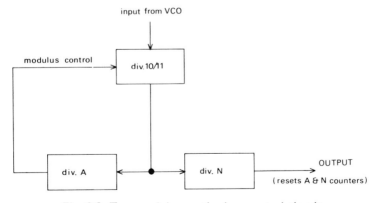

Fig. 6.3 Two modulus synthesiser control circuit

Two CMOS programmable counters (operating at one tenth of the VCO frequency) are connected to the output of the divide by 10/11 ECL divider. One counter is connected in series with the divider and increases the division ratio by a factor N. The ECL divider is normally set to divide by 10 and so (if the divide by A counter were absent) the overall division ratio would be 10 x N. But the divide by A counter can be programmed so that during the first part of the counting cycle the modulus control level can be changed. Since the divider is then temporarily set to divide by 11, for 'A' counts an extra A input cycles will be needed and the overall division ratio becomes $(10 \times N) + A$.

This provides a convenient way to divide at ECL speeds with programmable CMOS counters. The 'A' counter sets the units and 'N' the tens — which explains why divide by 10/11 is a popular choice. The obvious limitation is in input frequency; with a CMOS counter operating at 10 MHz it is clearly only suitable for a 100 MHz synthesiser. But by substituting a divide by 80/81 this problem can be overcome. To calculate the overall division ratio for any two modulus divide by $M/M+1$ divider the counters must first be assumed to have been reset to zero.

The division ratio is set to $(M + 1)$ for the first A counts; this corresponds to $A \times (M + 1)$ cycles of the input frequency. Then the modulus changes to M and the N counter continues to count up to N when it passes a pulse to the output. At this point both counters are reset, the ECL divider reverts to the $(M + 1)$ ratio and the cycle restarts. So the second half of the cycle counts $(N - A)$ x M cycles of the input frequency.

A full cycle of the system delivers one output pulse for each $A \times (M + 1)$ plus $(N - A) \times M$ input cycles. This can be reduced algebraically to a division ratio of $NM + A$. Remember that A cannot be greater than N. If the system is to be completely programmable (without gaps) then the A counter must count up to $(M - 1)$ at least. These two observations show that the minimum division ratio of the system must be when $M = N$ and the ECL divider is constantly dividing by the lower ratio ($A = 0$). Under these conditions the overall division ratio is $NM + A = NM = M^2$. A divide by 80/81 system for example, cannot be used for division ratios less than 80^2 (= 6400) and therefore in a 25 kHz channel spacing application is limited to a minimum of 160 MHz. There is clearly a conflict between the minimum overall division ratio and the requirement for a low input frequency for the CMOS counters, but this can normally be overcome by a suitable choice of components. Many other types of synthesisers are possible and their ranges can be extended using multipliers or mixers — but there are many publications on this subject. The two modulus ECL divider is at the heart of most synthesisers which operate above a few tens of MHz and this will now be examined in more detail.

Simple modulus divider

The simplest two modulus ECL divider on the market is a synchronous divide by 3/4, the Plessey SP8720. Its block diagram is shown in fig. 6.4. There are two modulus control inputs (market $\overline{PE1}$ and $\overline{PE2}$ in accordance with flip-flop terminology) and these are the inputs to an OR gate. When either or both inputs are high a 1 appears at the output of this gate; this is the divide by 3 configuration. The following AND gate is not affected and this allows a 1 at either Q1 or Q2 to be fed back to $\overline{D}$. Using the same notation as figs. 5.9 and 5.10 the truth table and timing diagram for this mode are shown in fig. 6.5.

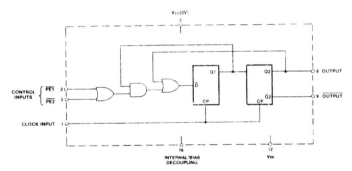

Fig. 6.4 Functional diagram of the SP8720

Assuming a starting state of Q1 = 0, Q2 = 0 the inversion caused by the $\overline{D}$ input causes the next state to become Q1 = 1, Q2 = 0. The same inversion causes Q1 to revert to 0 but Q2 now becomes 1; the next clock transition brings us back to the starting state. This is clearly the timing diagram of a divide by 3 function with an output mark/space of 1:2.

When both control inputs are low a 0 appears at the output of the first OR gate and this appears at the output of the AND gate, cutting off the feedback for Q1. The second OR gate is unaffected and the overall logic diagram is similar to that of fig. 5.9, a divide by 4 prescaler. The only effect of the modulus control input is to

Fig. 6.5 Truth table and timing diagram for divide by 3/4 (in divide by 3 mode)

Before		After	
Q1	Q2	Q1	Q2
0	0	1	0
0	1	0	0
1	0	0	1
*1	1	0	1

*Start-up condition only (since this condition does not appear in the 'after' table and cannot be the result of a normal counting sequence.)

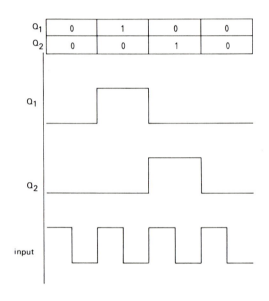

change the 'after' state of Q1 from 0 (divide by 3) to 1 (divide by 4) when the 'before' state is Q1 = 1, Q2 = 0. A composite timing diagram showing input and output only to illustrate this is shown in fig. 6.6.

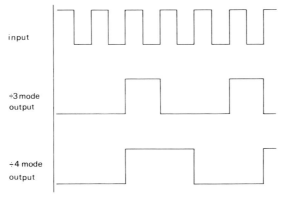

Fig. 6.6 Composite divide by 3/4 timing diagram

The next problem is to find out what happens when the divider is operating in one division mode and the control input is suddenly changed. This, after all, is what happens in the type of synthesiser already described. We have already seen that the control inputs are connected to a series of gates which affect the level of the D̄ input to the first flip-flop. They do not directly affect the state of either Q1 or Q2 and clearly no change in state can occur on a change of control input level until at least after the next positive transition of the clock input. We have also seen that the only 'after' state affected by the mode control is that corresponding to a 'before' state of Q1 = 1, Q2 = 0. Fig. 6.7 shows what happens when the modulus is changed from 3 to 4 under these conditions.

The result is that (ignoring gating delays for the time being) a control input change from high (divide by 3) to low (divide by 4) during the first two states of a cycle changes *that* cycle from divide by 3 to divide by 4. Only if, as drawn in fig. 6.7, the transition is delayed until the third stage does the effect take place in the following cycle. Changing from divide by 4 to divide by 3 is illustrated in fig. 6.8.

This is similar in that a transition of control input during the first half of the cycle ensures a change in that cycle. In the case illustrated the transition came too late (during the extra state which is unique to the divide by 4 configuration) and the change does not happen until the next cycle.

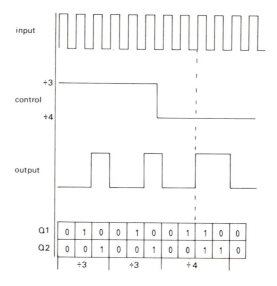

Fig. 6.7 Changing the modulus from 3 to 4

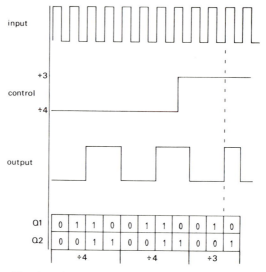

Fig. 6.8 Changing the modulus from 4 to 3

These diagrams assume a perfect divider with no internal time delays. In a practical situation there are, in addition to the clock to output (propagation) delay already described, delays between the change in level on the control input and the implementation of that change. These delays are known as 'set-up' and 'release' times.

Set-up time is measured between a point on the positive going edge of the control input and a point on the positive going edge of the next clock input to ensure that the new division mode (in this case divide by 3) is obtained. Release time is similarly specified but from a negative going edge of the control input. These times are normally very short − half the period of the input − and are frequently misunderstood. Set-up and release times are defined as minimum times, and do not imply that if the control input level is changed the appropriate number of ns before any clock transition, then at the transition the division ratio will immediately change. The ratio cannot change until the correct stage in the cycle, which may be half a cycle (and many clock transitions) later. This becomes very important when divide by 80/81 circuits are being considered! The purpose of these definitions is only to specify the internal gating delays. Fig. 6.9 illustrates the point.

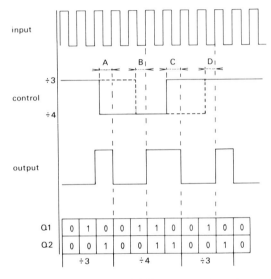

Fig. 6.9 Set-up and release times (a) This is *not* the release time (b) This is ... the control input transition could have been left to this point (c) This is *not* the set-up time (d) This is!

More two modulus dividers

Not all two modulus dividers are as simple as the divide by 3/4 function − and some are asynchronous. The divide by 10/11 Fairchild 11C90 shown in fig. 6.10 has three synchronous stages and an asynchronous output stage. There are facilities for setting the count to the extra (eleventh) state, for 'pulling up' the inputs (from TTL) and inhibiting the clock.

The 11C90 (575 MHz) is one of the fastest two modulus

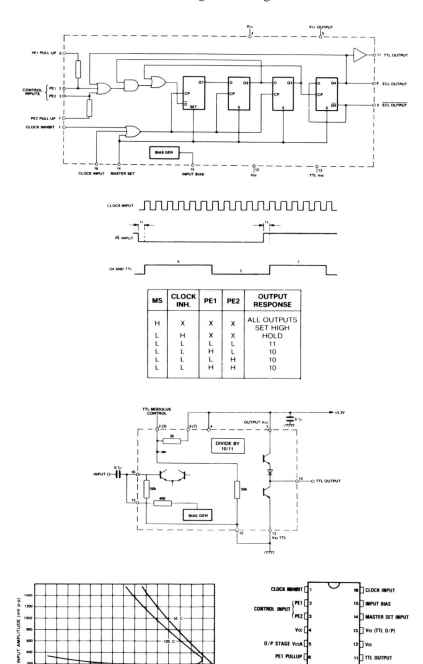

Fig. 6.10 11C90/SP8680

dividers on the open market, although technically it is now possible to manufacture products which exceed 1 GHz. There are other dividers incorporating a front end divide by 2 function ($M/M + 2$) such as the Plessey SP8786 (divide by 20/22, 1.3 GHz) but these may not have the same appeal to the synthesiser designer.

Many people do not realise that otherwise unobtainable two modulus division ratios can often be produced by extending the ratios of another device. No divide by 24/25 ratio is available on the open market — yet it can be produced by extending a divide by 3/4 with suitable divide by 8 prescaler. The simplest type of extension involves the use of an ECL (or even TTL) D type flip-flop at the output of the two modulus divider, with a connection to the modulus control input. This is one reason why most manufacturers provide two such inputs. Fig. 6.11 shows such an arrangement to extend a divide by 10/11 to divide by 20/21 (or any divide by $M/M + 1$ to divide by $2M/2M + 1$).

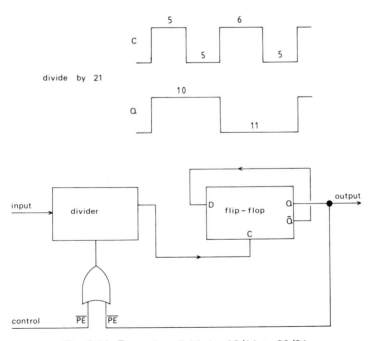

Fig. 6.11 Extending divide by 10/11 to 20/21

This circuit operates as follows. The $\overline{PE}$ inputs are such that both must be low for the divider to divide by 11, and if either is high then divide by 10 is selected. When the control input is set

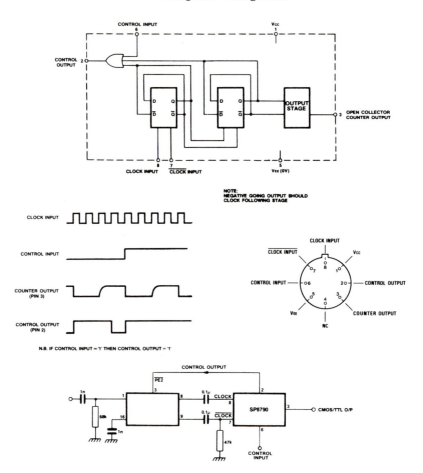

Fig. 6.12 SP8790 divide by 4 extender

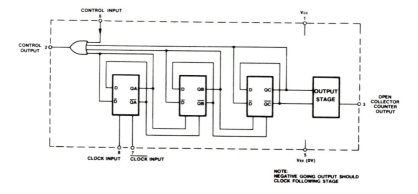

Fig. 6.13 SP8794 divide by 8 extender

high then the feedback from the output to $\overline{\text{PE}}$ has no effect. The divider divides by 10 and the flip-flop by 2, so the overall ratio is divide by 20.

When the control input is low the state of Q2 controls the division ratio. If Q2 starts high then the divide by 10 mode is selected. After 10 input cycles Q2 goes low and the divide by 11 mode comes into operation. The overall division ratio is 21. A similar result occurs if Q2 starts at 0.

The only problem with this type of configuration is that the propagation delay of the extra flip-flop adds to the set-up and release times. This is unfortunate because in a system working up to 200 MHz, for example, the flip-flop will never see more than 20 MHz and a TTL product might well have been chosen. But this could increase set-up and release times by a factor of 10! Special low power ECL extenders are available to overcome this problem, and the Plessey SP8790 and SP8794 are examples. See figs. 6.12 and 6.13.

Synthesiser timing

The choice of two modulus division ratio is not only determined by what is available; there is a trade off between:

Low division ratio	High division ratio
Counting speed too high for MOS	Can use low cost MOS counters
Low minimum count	Minimum count too high to cover range

Ease of programming is also important; with a divide by 10/11 the counters set tens and units of division ratio and can save unnecessary decoding elsewhere in the circuitry. The final decision, especially at high frequency is based on a calculation of the time delays in the divider and a counter to make sure that there is sufficient time to change the modulus before the next cycle starts. This is shown in fig. 6.14 where the concept of loop delay, the period during which a decision to change can be made, is introduced.

The cycle is assumed to start with the A and N counters reset and the divider set to divide by $(M + 1)$, 4 in this case. After the A counter is filled there is a period of time during which the output of the A counter must rise to ensure the correct count of M (3) in the following cycle. This period of time, the loop delay, can be calculated by subtracting the divider propagation (clock to output) delay and set-up time from the output period. With an input frequency of 120 MHz, for example, the output period is 33 ns which with the SP8720 allows a loop delay of 29 ns. This precludes the use of MOS!

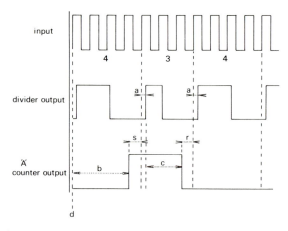

Fig. 6.14 Loop delay with divide by 3/4 (a) divider propagation delay (b) maximum propagation delay of 'A' counter (c) maximum propagation delay of 'N' counter (d) this is the A'th output pulse of the divider (r) release time (s) set-up time

But a more serious situation arises at the end of the count cycle when the N counter has been filled. Its output is used to reset the A counter output to zero, but because of the lower division ratio during this part of the cycle the loop delay is even shorter. At 120 MHz the output period is only 25 ns and this leaves only 14 ns. Since this time must cover both the propagation delay of the N counter and the time to reset the A counter it is clear that ECL counters must be used with this exceptionally low division ratio. In fact the SP8720 has only ECL compatible inputs for this reason. A more typical example would be the use of a divide by 40/41 divider at 200 MHz, where of the 200 ns period more than 130 ns is normally available for the MOS counters.

A point worth mentioning is that all dividers and counters until now are assumed to clock on the 0 to 1 (positive going) input edge. If positive edge dividers are used with negative edge counters, for example, only half the divider output period is available and loop delays are dramatically shortened. Unless there is a special reason these two edges should not be mixed. There is one advantage in using negative edge triggering throughout the system although few dividers offer this feature. Fig. 5.18 illustrates an

open collector output stage of the type normally used for interfacing with MOS counters. The positive going edge is very slow
because it takes some tens of nanoseconds to charge the load
capacitance through the high valued load resistance. The negative
edge is much sharper because the output transistor ON resistance
is small. The difference in a real system is very considerable and it
seems surprising that so few products take advantage of this. The
reason, I am told, is only that of convention!

Dedicated synthesisers

We have already seen that the digital part of frequency synthesisers
can be designed around an ECL two modulus divider and two
MOS or CMOS counters. The VCO, buffer, filter and any other
linear function such as a modulator are also needed as is some type
of memory to store the A and N counts required. Often an interface is needed to accept inputs of channel numbers from a key-
board and translate them into division ratios. The complete design
of such synthesisers is clearly well outside the scope of a publica-
tion on ECL but it is worth while to review some of the options
available to the designer.

Most ECL manufacturers are aware of the difficulty of synthesiser design and are anxious to integrate as much as possible of the
circuitry into one or more ICs. These dedicated synthesiser sets
should be your first choice; they can save dramatically on circuit
design costs and offer adequate performance for most applications. They can be grouped conveniently into three categories as
follows:

(a) sets of bipolar ICs for the complete function;
(b) two chip (bipolar + MOS) for divider chain only;
(c) single chip (ECL + I^2L) including most of function.

The first category was dominant until about 1980, and some
products have since been discontinued. Typical of these were the
early bipolar CB radio synthesisers (with channel information and
division ratios built-in) which have now been replaced by better
CMOS versions. These sets often used the ECL3 MC/SP 1648
oscillator as a VCO, using an external varicap diode. Despite a
slightly inferior noise level the 1648 is still a good choice up to
150 MHz where the ultimate in performance is not needed. Fig.
6.15 shows a typical circuit configuration.

The 1648 can cover a 4:1 frequency range without difficulty

provided that suitable tuning diodes are used. The output is ECL compatible (ideal for dividers) but can be modified to a sine wave by connecting a resistor between pin 5, the AGC decoupling point, and negative supply. By using a 9 V supply to the output pin and a tuned load to about 900 Ω it is possible to generate an output power of 5 to 10 mW.

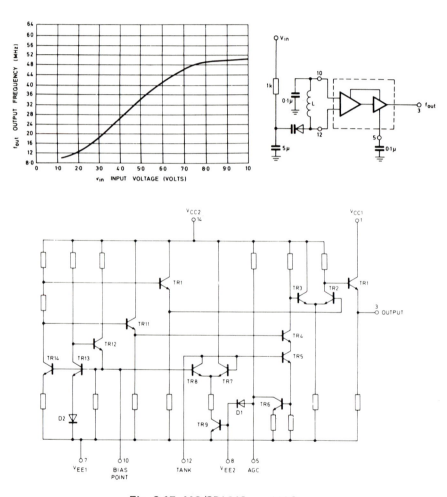

Fig. 6.15 MC/SP1648 as a VCO

Another component of synthesisers is the phase/frequency detector which performs the task of comparing the crystal reference with the output of the divider chain. In most present day applications this comparison takes place at the frequency of the channel spacing – between 5 and 50 kHz – and the use of

ECL is superfluous. But there are some synthesiser design techniques which require better performance and Motorola produce an ECL phase/frequency detector which operates at over 50 MHz, the MC12040. This is shown in fig. 6.16. Similar TTL detectors are available from the same company (MC4044) and Fairchild (11C44).

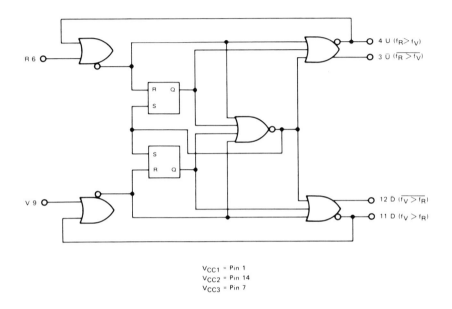

$$V_{CC1} = Pin\ 1$$
$$V_{CC2} = Pin\ 14$$
$$V_{CC3} = Pin\ 7$$

Fig. 6.16 MC12040 phase/frequency detector

These detectors are all based on the comparison of the outputs of two D type flip-flops, one triggered from the crystal oscillator and the other from the divider chain. The output pulse duration corresponds to the difference in timing (and hence phase angle) between the two inputs.

Another similar circuit is the Plessey SP8760, a single chip divide by 15/16, crystal oscillator and phase/frequency detector function.

Many separate crystal oscillator circuits are available – they can be constructed from transistors, standard logic gates or special ICs. A few use ECL technology but they are not widely used.

Other synthesiser functions available in ECL technology are limited to logic functions (ECL3 or ECL10K) but a special D type flip-flop, the Motorola MC12000, is used for digital mixing in more specialised types of synthesiser design. Other logic functions worthy of mention include the ECL10K 10536/7 125 MHz synchronous counters which have propagation delays of less than 5 ns.

ECL + MOS synthesisers

The so-called 'two chip' synthesisers which have been introduced recently are probably the best choice for the majority of applications. They often incorporate extra features such as integral crystal oscillators or the ability to control division ratios and channel spacings from an external microprocessor. In addition their volume sales into the consumer or professional mobile and handheld radio markets mean a lower price. One chip performs the high frequency division using ECL bipolar technology. The second, using CMOS or any other MOS technology, integrates the A and N counters and phase/frequency comparator together with the interfacing or control circuitry. Most incorporate a facility to load and store the division ratio required.

Since we are primarily concerned with the ECL divider there is no point in looking in detail at each of the systems on the market. A typical example is the Motorola MC145156 which can operate with dividers with ratios from divide by 3/4 to divide by 128/129. It is shown in fig. 6.17.

The MC145156 accepts serial input data for programming the A and N counters. Two shift registers and a clock input are provided, along with two latches to store the count. A third counter R is included to divide the output of the integral crystal oscillator circuit to the desired channel spacing; three inputs are provided to select one of 8 division ratios. The A counter has 7 bits and hence can count from 0 to 127 ($2^7 - 1$); this means it can control up to a two modulus divide by 128/9 divider. The N counter has a maximum count of 1023 ($2^{10} - 1$). Although the circuit can accept input frequencies over 15 MHz the limitation is really that of propagation delay from input to modulus control output, stated as 100 ns (at 5 V). This must be added to the propagation and set-up times of the divider to determine the maximum input frequency — probably about 7 MHz. So with a divide by 40/41 it should be possible to operate up to 280 MHz. The input is clocked on the positive edge and should therefore be used with ECL dividers which also clock on the positive edge.

A typical application of another synthesiser kit, the Plessey

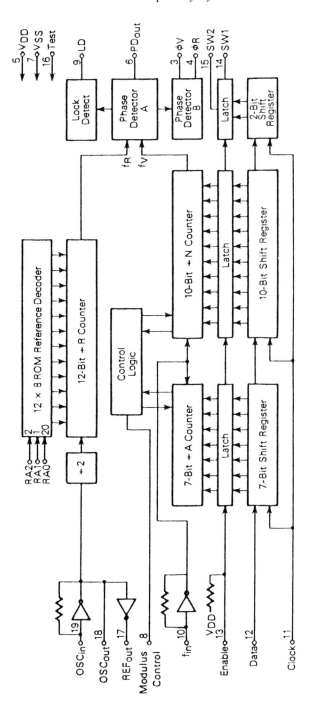

Fig. 6.17 Motorola two chip synthesiser

NJ8812/SP8793, is shown in fig. 6.18.

One system a little different from the others is the Plessey SP8906 (bipolar) and NJ8811 (NMOS) set shown in fig. 6.19.

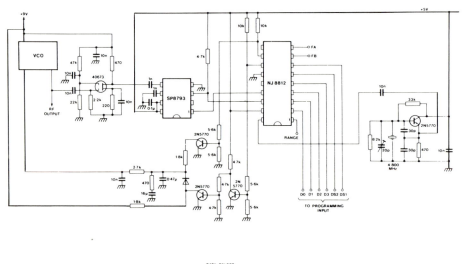

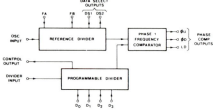

Fig. 6.18 Using the NJ8812/SP8793

The SP8906 is a four modulus divider; its ratio is 239/240/255/256. The advantage of this technique is that a wider frequency range can be covered than with a two modulus divider – provided, of course, that a suitable VCO is available. The SP8906 can operate over an 18:1 range, more than twice that of a comparable simpler divider.

Other techniques of interest mainly relate to the MOS control circuitry. New high speed CMOS technology allows the input frequency to the A and N counters to rise above 10 MHz, allowing the use of lower two modulus division ratios. More advanced 'sample and hold' type phase comparators (first introduced by Philips on their HEF4751) allow locking times as low as 5 ms (rather than 200 ms) to be achieved. 'Fast hopping' synthesisers are becoming a reality. 'Fractional N' synthesisers offer similar advantages, with phase comparison at frequencies higher than normally attainable. Specialised TV synthesisers incorporate a whole host of features needed for that market, including a fine tuning (AFC) control, on-screen display and non-volatile channel memory.

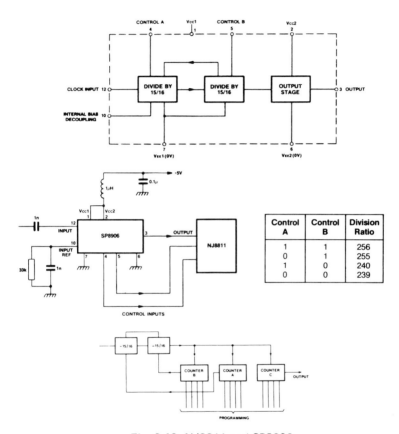

Fig. 6.19 NJ8811 and SP8906

But what today is possible using two ICs may well be possible tomorrow in one.

Since ECL bipolar and MOS technology cannot easily be combined on one chip, either MOS has to operate at a high frequency or ECL has to be combined with low power counter circuitry, probably in 'integrated injection logic' (I^2L). Both approaches have been demonstrated and either or both may be successful in years to come. An NMOS synthesiser operating at 220 MHz has been put into production by Sony in Japan and

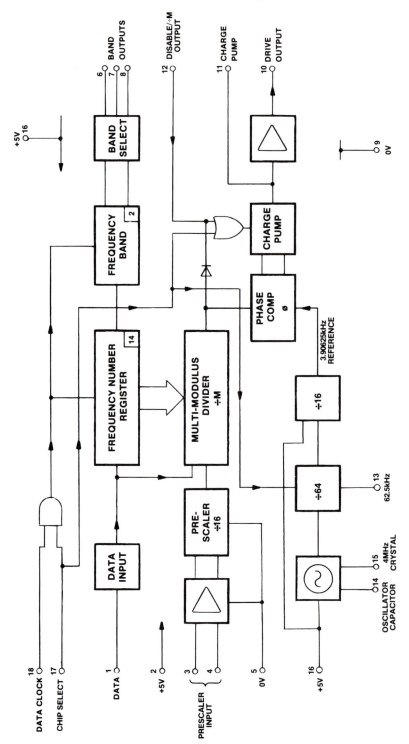

Fig. 6.20 SP5000 TV synthesiser

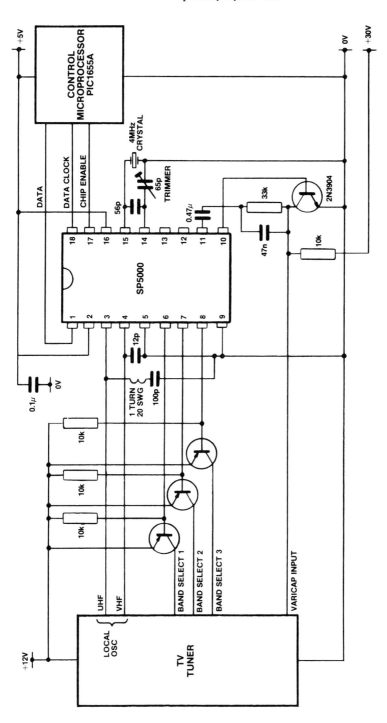

Fig. 6.21 Using the SP5000

it is used in a fully synthesised AM/FM hi-fi tuner.

The alternative approach, the combination of ECL and I²L, has recently entered production in the form of a TV frequency synthesiser circuit from Plessey. The SP5000 is a relatively complex circuit as can be seen from fig. 6.20.

The SP5000 consists of five main parts — a divide by 16 prescaler in ECL, a 14 bit programmable divider, a phase comparator, a crystal oscillator and a serially loaded data register. The power supply is only 65 mA at 5.0 V and the IC is available in an 18 lead plastic package. Sensitivity at 1 GHz is 200 mV peak-peak maximum, this being achieved by means of an on-board preamplifier. A typical application involving band selection is shown in fig. 6.21. In this application the frequency information is obtained from a microprocessor with internal read-only memory (ROM) containing the appropriate data.

The SP5000 is the first of many products of this type; the combination of ECL, I²L and linear technology on one IC is an ideal solution for TV synthesis. The professional market has rather different requirements, however, and it may be some time before circuits of this type become available.

CHAPTER 7
Data conversion

The voltage comparators in the ECL3 family are only the beginning of a wide range of comparators and analogue to digital converters (ADCs). Corresponding digital to analogue converters (DACs) have also been developed.

ECL technology adapts well to the design of comparators. By convention the input and reference voltages to be compared lie around 0 V (normally within a 'common mode range' from -2 V to $+2$ V or so) and the comparator can therefore operate conveniently from supply voltages of $+5$ V and -5.2 V. This presents a problem with the limited voltage ratings of some fast bipolar processes and it is important to observe the maximum ratings for each product. The fastest comparators on the market have a propagation delay (from input to output) of only 2 ns and even faster products are being developed.

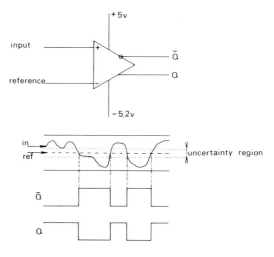

Fig. 7.1 Simple voltage comparator

Fig. 7.1 shows a diagram of a simple comparator (without a latch) and the waveforms associated with it. Timing delays have been neglected to avoid complication.

The comparator has two inputs. The '+' input (non-inverting) is normally connected to the variable input, the '−' input to the reference. The diagram shows the relationship between input and output voltage, especially the region of uncertainty (normally about ± 10 mV) during which the output state is not defined. This uncertainty is composed of two separate items − the imbalance of the comparator and the need to provide a minimum voltage to achieve the output swing (this is a function of the voltage gain of the comparator). The imbalance depends partly on external circuitry and is normally specified as the sum of a voltage offset and a current offset; the latter becomes a voltage offset on flowing through the input resistors. A typical offset would be ± 5 mV plus ± 5 μA. With an external DC input resistance of 1 kΩ between each input and 0 V this gives a total offset of ± 10 mV. If the resistance paths are unequal there will be a further offset due to the effect of input bias currents. Strictly speaking an additional allowance should be made for the change in offset voltage within the common mode range (calculated from the common mode rejection ratio, CMRR) and the supply voltage range (supply voltage rejection ratio, SVRR) but this is normally insignificant. The reader should refer to publications on the subject of operational amplifiers for an explanation of these ratios.

The voltage gain of a comparator is normally at least 40 dB (x 100) so an ECL output swing of 800 mV would require only 8 mV input (overdrive) once imbalance has been overcome, so an input voltage of at least 18 mV above or 18 mV below the reference input will fully switch the comparator (in this example). A data sheet would probably specify switching speeds with 20 mV inputs, indicating the change (normally improvement) with increasing overdrive. In some applications it is important to define what will happen if the input level is too low and there are at least two techniques for this.

Hysteresis is a technique of moving the reference voltage slightly according to the output state of the comparator. Fig. 2.13 illustrates this inbuilt feature of the MC/SP1650, but it is possible in theory to apply hysteresis to any comparator so that the output state will not change until the input is moved out of the uncertainty region. This is not always easy at ECL speeds.

A second method is the provision of a 'latch' input. When the latch is applied (a logic level) the gain of the comparator is effectively increased by internal application of positive feedback so that the output is forced into one logic state. This state is then held regardless of any subsequent input level change until the latch is turned off. Fig. 7.2 shows the timing diagram of a latched comparator.

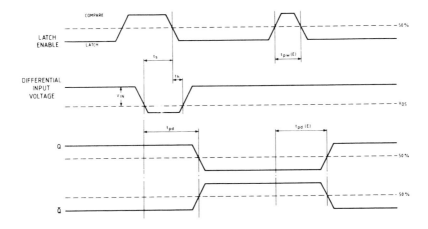

Fig. 7.2 Comparator timing diagram

In this case the latch is set to compare ('strobe') when '1', latch when '0'. A minimum latch pulse width — shown here as $t_{pw}(E)$ — is required for the latch to cease to have an effect. Propagation delays are shown both for unlatched mode (t_{pd}) and for change to occur after latch removed ($t_{pd}(E)$). Latch set-up (t_s) and hold times (t_h) are also shown; the input signal must occur at a time t_s before the latch falling edge and must be maintained for a time t_h after the latch falling edge in order to be 'acquired'.

Fig. 7.3 List of ECL comparators

	1650	9680	9685	9687
Manufacturers	Motorola Plessey	Plessey	Plessey Analog D	Plessey Analog D
Supply voltages	+5, −5.2 V	+5, −5.2 V	+5, −5.2 V	+5, −5.2 V
Latch	latch	−	latch	latch
Single/dual	dual	single	single	dual
Hysteresis	Yes	No	No	No
Maximum delay	5 ns	4 ns	3 ns	3 ns

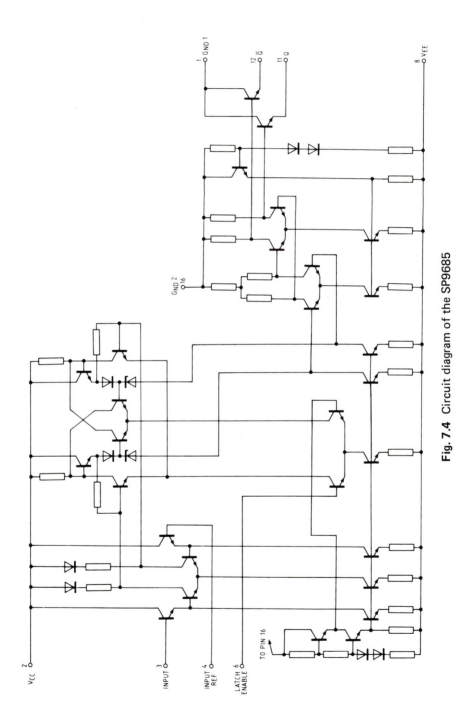

Fig. 7.4 Circuit diagram of the SP9685

The choice between using latched or unlatched comparators with or without hysteresis really depends on whether or not you know when the output state must be defined. Latched comparators are probably more popular but not as simple to use. One less important advantage of comparators with hysteresis is their freedom from oscillation; they do not behave as amplifiers until a certain input level is reached!

Fig. 7.3 lists the important details of popular ECL comparators; fig. 7.4 shows the circuit diagram of the fastest commercially available product, the Plessey SP9685.

Although most applications of voltage comparators are simple it is possible to use the circuits to perform functions such as window detection, line receiving or even as oscillators. Fig. 7.5 shows the use of a latched comparator to detect the presence of a 10 mV, 3 ns pulse; to reset the circuit it is necessary to remove the power supplies.

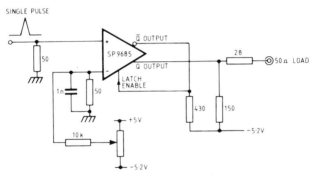

Fig. 7.5 Short pulse detector

Analogue to digital conversion

A simple comparator indicates the presence or absence of an input signal (with reference to a fixed voltage) and in that sense it may be said to act as an analogue to digital converter. A more general example requires the use of several comparators each connected to the same input, but with different reference voltages. The input (analogue) signal can then be specified as being in one of $(N+1)$ regions, where N is the number of comparators (see fig. 7.6).

The three comparators together define the four regions (below -1 V, between -1 V and 0 V, between 0 V and $+1$ V, and above $+1$ V). The outputs A, B and C are capable of more logical combinations than the circuit allows; in fact they can be gated together to provide just two outputs with the following coding:

Input	A	B
Under −1 V	0	0
−1 V to 0 V	0	1
0 V to +1 V	1	0
Above +1 V	1	1

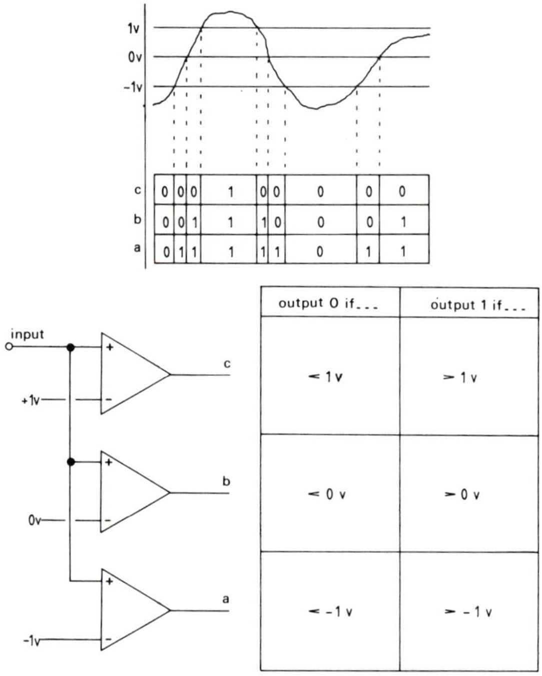

Fig. 7.6 Analogue to digital conversion

The purpose of this binary encoding is to simplify subsequent digital processing – in this example the input has been split ('quantised') into four levels and encoded as a 2 bit binary digital signal. Most applications call for 8 or even 10 bits (at ECL speeds) and since N bits require (2^N-1) comparators this is both difficult and extremely expensive to achieve in a single integrated circuit. New developments in technology are eagerly awaited.

Meanwhile there are many different methods of analogue to digital conversion which reduce the number of comparators per bit – and, sadly, the speed of conversion. For reference, the method just described is known as all-parallel (or 'flash') conversion and is shown in fig. 7.7.

The next technique is the parallel-series (or 'subranging') converter. Conveniently applied to 8 bit conversion, the principle is to employ two separate 4 bit converters. The first quantises the four most significant bits of the input. Its output is then converted back to analogue, subtracted from the original input (to get the second four bits) and applied to the second 4 bit converter. The advantage is that only 30 (not 255) comparators are needed; the disadvantages lie in the complexity and very considerable difficulty in board layout to avoid timing problems. Fig. 7.8 shows a block diagram which includes an analogue 'sample-and-hold' circuit to keep the input level constant during conversion.

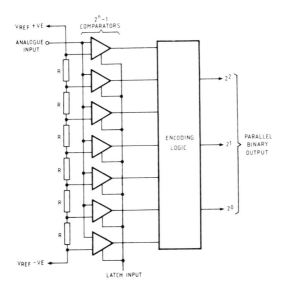

Fig. 7.7 All-parallel conversion

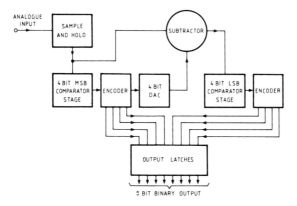

Fig. 7.8 Parallel-series conversion

Because two separate conversions take place the complexity increases dramatically and the simple, almost symmetrical arrangement of all-parallel conversion is lost. Parallel-series converters are not manufactured as single integrated circuits but as a board or thick film hybrid; each block of fig. 7.8 is realisable as a single IC although this may not be the best or easiest solution. The sample-and-hold, for example, is frequently constructed from a Schottky diode ring followed by a fast operational amplifier. The subtractor is often a buffer amplifier made from transistors rather than an IC. The timing and hence layout of each part of the circuit is carefully calculated to ensure that each group of 4 bits arrives together; the output latch stores the first 4 bits until the rest arrive. A practical circuit may incorporate extra features such as tapped delay lines or extra buffers to optimise the performance. Considerable skill is required to design a high speed parallel-series converter.

As a guide to assessing the relative performance of different types of ADC (analogue to digital converter), a simple all-parallel converter is capable of over 100 MHz operation with an accuracy of 8 bits whereas a parallel-series converter built with similar components can only achieve 30 MHz or so. It is theoretically possible to extend the parallel-series principle to three stages – say 3 + 3 + 3 for 9 bit accuracy – but at this point the speed is reduced further and the following technique becomes more attractive.

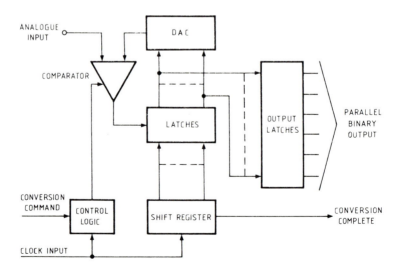

Fig. 7.9 Successive approximation conversion

The 'successive approximation' converter is, as the name suggests, a technique in which the output signal changes, becoming progressively more accurate until conversion is complete. It is, in fact, a one bit converter (a single comparator) with some memory, control logic and an accurate digital to analogue converter (DAC). The diagram of fig. 7.9 shows how these are connected. Although the principles of this conversion technique are easy to grasp it is not quite as simple to understand the block diagram. Fig. 7.10 provides a better explanation.

Fig. 7.10 Principles of successive approximation

Levels					
	7	1	1	1	
	6	1	1	0	
	5	1	0	1	
	4	1	0	0	Binary
	3	0	1	1	output
	2	0	1	0	
	1	0	0	1	
	0	0	0	0	
		MSB		LSB	

Suppose the input is in level 5

First conversion gives output	100
Second conversion gives output	100
Third conversion gives output	101

The diagram relates to a 3 bit (8 level) ADC for simplicity but the principle can easily be extended to a larger number of bits. The eight input level regions ('steps') have been numbered from 0 to 7 to correspond with the binary output. Examine the pattern of zeros and ones in the binary output – for the lower 4 input levels the MSB is 0, for the upper 4 it is 1. Clearly, if only one bit were available, the MSB would indicate in which half of the voltage range the input would be. By adding the next bit this would be narrowed down to the quarter, then the eighth, and so on. So a converter which first provides the MSB and then the next least significant bits in sequence is successively approximating the output.

Referring back to fig. 7.9, the circuitry is arranged to set the latches and shift register to zero when conversion begins. At the next clock pulse a 1 appears in the MSB position of the shift register (and therefore the latch). The DAC converts this back to analogue and the comparator gives an output of 1 or 0 depending on whether the analogue input is greater or less than the DAC output. The comparator output then corrects the latch level if necessary and the process is repeated on the next bit.

A successive approximation ADC is a little easier to design and build than a parallel-series converter, but layout is still critical. Apart from the comparator, DAC and output latches it is possible to buy a 'successive approximation register' which integrates most of the circuitry. An 8 bit converter of this type operates at approximately one-ninth of the speed of an all-parallel design (approximately 12 MHz with present day technology).

There are other types of converter which incorporate a DAC in the 'feedback loop'. An example is the tracking (or servocounting) converter in which the shift register and latches are replaced by an up/down counter controlled from the comparator output. Although slower (because up/down counters are not fast enough) it is an ideal converter for use when monitoring a relatively stable input voltage as it responds quickly to small input level changes.

Another type of ADC of limited application is the peak detecting ADC. Ideal for digitising the voltage level of a short pulse, this is a good technique for nucleonics and instrumentation converters. It is based on the short pulse detector circuit of fig. 7.5 but with several comparators interconnected as for all-parallel conversion (see fig. 7.7). As before, a digital output corresponding to the input amplitude is obtained.

There are many other ADC design techniques – but those mentioned above seem most suited to ECL technology. Products available today are as follows:

2, 4, 6, 8 and 10 bit all-parallel ADCs
latches up to 8 bits
comparators
up/down counters up to 8 bits
successive approximation registers for 8 and 10 bits
DACs up to 10 bits

Fig. 7.11 details the ECL ADC products on the market.

The majority of ADC applications involve the continuous sampling and digitisation of an input waveform. In theory an ADC must convert at twice the highest input frequency or more in order to reproduce the waveform faithfully. Strictly speaking the comparison should be made of 'data rates' (and these are expressed in mega samples per second instead of MHz). The terminology of ADC data sheets includes several terms worthy of further examination. Unfortunately there is a lack of standardisation of both terminology and test methods but the following terms should at least offer a starting point.

Fig. 7.11 List of ECL ADC products

Manufacturer	Product	No. of bits	Maximum sample rate (MHz)
Analog	AD5010	6	100
Devices	AD6020	6	50
(Siemens)			
AMD	AM6688	4	100
Matsushita	(to be announced)	8	40
Motorola	MC10317	7	15
Plessey	SP9754	4	100
Sony	CX20052	8	30 (parallel-series)
TRW	TDC10XXJ	8	75 (CML)
	TDC1029J	6	100 (CML)

Accuracy (e.g. 8 bits) may seem obvious, but when building a parallel-series converter — say, 4+4 bits — you need 8 bits of accuracy in a 4 bit ADC.

Aperture uncertainty relates to the precise time at which each bit is compared. Any 'jitter' in this time causes different bits to be sampled at different times, causing an error if the input voltage is changing rapidly (if the slew rate of the input signal is high). The value of aperture uncertainty is normally a few tens of picoseconds.

Conversion time is normally related to the sample rate and may not be quoted.

Linearity errors are of two types. 'Integral non-linearity' occurs when the analogue to digital transfer function deviates from a straight line, causing distortion. The effect is most serious for high level signals.

'Differential non-linearity' is the result of a single quantisation step differing from the correct value and causes a kink in the transfer function at that point. The effect is most serious for low level signals.

Monotonic. An ADC is said to be 'monotonic' if there is a digital output for every input level in the range and if, as the input is increased progressively, the output never falls. An ADC which is not monotonic would usually be considered to be faulty.

Missing codes. If for some reason an ADC has severe non-linearity it is possible that one of the steps could be missed completely. Again, this is a serious fault.

Noise is a combination of many factors. 'Quantisation noise' between an analogue signal and its digitised form is simply the result of having finite steps in the waveform. More bits, less noise. Some noise effects are translatable into aperture uncertainty (phase noise), linearity errors and missing codes.

Nyquist rate is a sample rate of exactly twice the maximum input frequency.

Quantisation error is the sum of the error caused by having a finite number of steps in the first place and of the differential non-linearity.

Sample rate (in megasamples per second) is the normal indication of the speed of an ADC.

Video speed is a term applied to an ADC which can handle a maximum input frequency of at least 7 MHz (normal TV video band width). A normal all-parallel video speed converter needs a sample rate of 15 MHz or more.

Analogue to digital conversion at high speeds is rapidly becoming a specialised subject; the relationship between analogue effects such as 'phase error' and the digital (?) causes (which may simply be layout problems) could take years to study.

Digital to analogue conversion

Once an analogue signal has been digitised it can be processed, stored in memory and analysed but eventually it may be converted back. High speed DACs are therefore essential to complement the ADCs — in fact some forms of ADCs are based on DACs anyway. ECL technology favours a current switching DAC rather than the conventional R/2R ladder networks employed at lower speeds and fig. 7.12 illustrates this.

By suitable choice of reference voltage (V_{REF}) the constant current sink can be made to draw all its current from the output when the input is at 0, and to draw all its current from the input transistor when at 1. The current sink in the case is a transistor permanently biased from another reference voltage (see fig. 7.13).

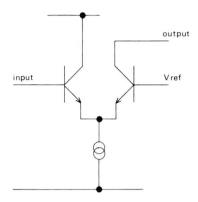

Fig. 7.12 DAC current switch

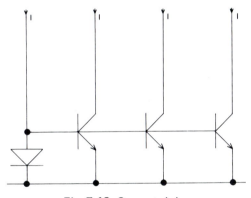

Fig. 7.13 Current sink

Provided that the diode and transistors have identical geometries and are at the same temperature then the currents in each device are almost exactly equal (they have the same $V_{BE(ON)}$ for a given I_C). The diode is simply a transistor with collector and base linked together. It is also easy to connect a number of transistors together — or design a transistor with a larger emitter area — to sink, say, twice or four times I.

This is where the design adapts to digital to analogue conversion. Consider an 8 bit digital input; if all bits are zero then there is no output from the DAC. If the LSB is 1 the output could be, say, 1 mV. The next most significant bit corresponds to two LSBs, the next to four, and so on. Each bit has a value in mV, ranging from the LSB (1 mV) to the MSB (128 mV). When the bit

is 1 its value should be added to the output. At maximum input
(11111111) the output voltage should be (128 + 64 + 32 + 16 + 8
+ 4 + 2 + 1) mV.

All that is necessary is to connect each of the input bits to a
current switch and to sum the currents at the output. Fig. 7.14
shows how this can be done.

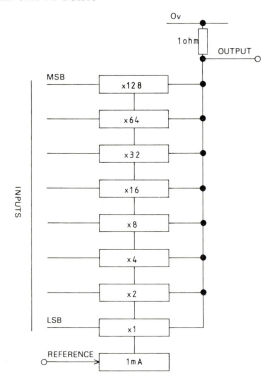

Fig. 7.14 A simple 8 bit DAC

A practical DAC would operate with lower currents and into a
50 Ω nominal output — probably also of alternate polarity. It is
worth pointing out that the reference input current does not have
to be a DC current. Since this type of DAC is effectively multiplying (digitally) the reference input it can be used to multiply a
high frequency sine wave, for example. One DAC, the Plessey
SP9768, has a quoted multiplying bandwidth of 40 MHz and it
can be used for controlling the amplitude of signal generators
and the like.

Where a reference is needed, however, it can be provided on
or off the chip by using a zener diode type of voltage regulator fed
from a constant current source. This provides a constant voltage

from which it is relatively easy to derive a constant current of a suitable level.

Current switched DACs of the type described here tend to suffer from a problem common to all parallel transistor switches – unequal switching speeds. Consider the case when the input changes from a low level to a high level. In a badly designed DAC the switches will change one by one, over a period of several nanoseconds, perhaps causing a temporary output level below the original low or above the final high level. Eventually the output will settle at the correct value. These temporary output level excursions are known as 'glitches' and can be caused either by unequal switching delays or stray capacitive coupling. Many DAC integrated circuits suffer from glitch problems, mainly because the transistor current switches for each input bit are of different sizes and switch different currents (1, 2, 4, 8 etc.). This can only be avoided by subdividing the switches into units, each of which pass the same current. Fig. 7.15 shows a simplified circuit diagram of an 8 bit DAC which has this feature. The circuit also incorporates a temperature sensing transistor pair within the current switch network; temperature changes are signalled back to the bias network to stabilise the output current.

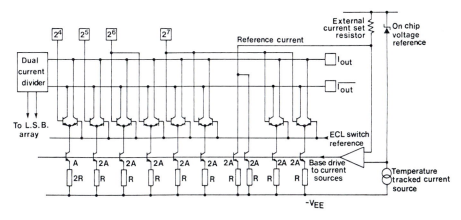

Fig. 7.15 Partial circuit diagram of the SP9768

The high speed DAC market, previously dominated by hybrid ECL3 designs, is now served by many different monolithic ICs. Prices have fallen to the point where it is easier and cheaper to use an IC. Products available today are detailed in fig. 7.16.

Many DAC data sheets include terms already described for ADCs but the following are often included as well:

Fig. 7.16 List of ECL DAC products

Manufacturer	Product	No. of bits	Settling time (to ½ LSB, ns)
Analog	HDS0810E	8	10
Devices	HDS1015E	10	15
	HDS1240E	12	40
Motorola	MC10318	8	10
Plessey	SP9768	8	5
Sony	CX20051	10	–
TRW	TDC1016J	8	– (CML)
	TDC1017J	10	– (CML)

Bit size defines the change in output current (or voltage) caused
by a change in the least significant bit (LSB). In the case of an
8 bit DAC it is the full scale output swing divided by 256.

Compliance describes the range of output voltage over which the
DAC can operate while still supplying the specified output
currents. It is important because this current is converted into a
voltage by the load resistor.

Settling time is the time taken for the output of a DAC to respond
to an input change. It is normally measured for the change from
zero to maximum input and defined as shown in fig. 7.17.

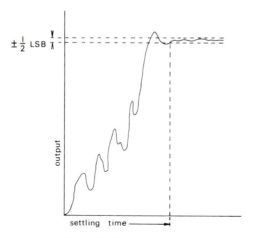

Fig. 7.17 DAC settling time

Temperature coefficient of an internal reference is important.
Check that the error will not be significant over the required

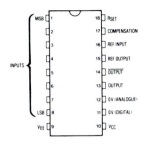

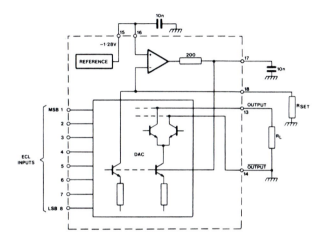

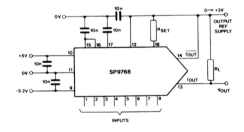

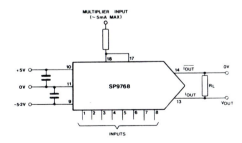

Fig. 7.18 SP9678 DAC

temperature range of operation; 30p.p.m./C° is probably adequate.

Fig. 7.18 shows a block diagram of a fast 8 bit ECL DAC, the Plessey SP9768.

Applications of ECL data conversion circuits

High speed data conversion is relatively new and it is difficult to identify all possible areas of application. We do know the effect that ADCs and DACs have had on, say, the telephone communications market — where the IC content of new equipment has changed in five years from almost all analogue to almost all digital. At the higher speeds made possible by ECL this type of mass market has yet to emerge, but the relative ease of measuring, storing, processing and transmitting in a digital format is very attractive. One of the first areas of application has been in the professional TV market — in 'special effects' studio equipment and in simplified TV cameras or control equipment. Many people believe that a digital TV system will emerge one day (perhaps using CMOS rather than ECL technology) but a digital video tape recording system cannot be far away.

Domestic TV requires data rates of only 15 megasamples per second and 8 bit accuracy, so ECL is not the only solution. Possible ADC configurations are:

(a) parallel-series (4+4) — ECL
(b) all-parallel (8) — CMOS or ECL
(c) successive approximation — ECL

and all have been successfully demonstrated. The major limitation is price, but there are many technical snags which make it difficult to use many circuits available today. A minor shift of phase, for example, can ruin picture quality. The DAC is even more critical and glitch-free performance is essential. Most TV display systems today use a 'raster scan' technique where the DAC controls the brightness of the beam. Fig. 7.19 illustrates how this is done. An 8 bit system allows a 256 level 'grey scale' which is considered adequate.

Other graphics applications include instrumentation and radar displays, where it is useful to have titles, scale values etc. added to CRT displays. Some equipments have facilities to (digitally) enlarge sections of the display and to store details for subsequent replay. Storage oscilloscopes using semiconductor memory are emerging in competition with traditional storage tubes; they offer indefinite storage time, allow timebase expansion after capture and can often be interfaced to chart recorders for provision of printed output. Such equipments need up to 8 or 10 bits of data with conversion at the fastest rate possible. Future developments will include direct interface with digital flat screen displays.

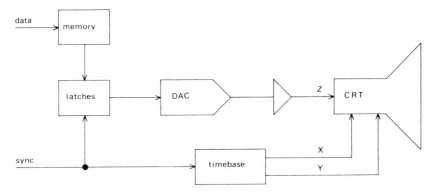

Fig. 7.19 Using a DAC for TV display

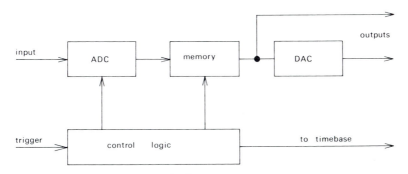

Fig. 7.20 Transient recorder

An extension of the digital storage technique is the transient recorder shown in fig. 7.20. A transient recorder is designed to record a short electrical impulse at very high speeds (sample rates of up to 500 MSPS are typical at 8 or 10 bits). The impulse is recorded in semiconductor memory and then replayed later at a relatively slow speed into an oscilloscope or chart recorder. A trigger signal is stored in memory to identify the time at which the impulse occurred but, unlike a conventional oscilloscope which uses the trigger to start the timebase, it is perfectly possible to observe and analyse an event before the trigger pulse. Transient recorders can also be used in conjunction with digital data processing systems and for this purpose a digital output is normally made available.

Another application of ECL data converters is in the generation of complex waveforms. A high speed microcomputer system can generate a series of digital words which, when converted to analogue using a high speed DAC (8 bit), can simulate an almost unlimited variety of pulses and waveforms.

These applications are almost unique to ECL data conversion circuits but many other lower speed applications can be adapted to run at higher data rates. As more new circuits are introduced the number of application possibilities will increase.

CHAPTER 8
Signal processing

As ECL becomes faster with improvements in technology there are
signs that a new and important digital signal processing market is
beginning to emerge. An extension of the data conversion technique already discussed, the methods described in this chapter
allow digitised data to be analysed, perhaps to search for a particular coded sequence of signals without necessarily ever being
converted back to analogue. Radar and military applications will
be far reaching, leading to the development of completely new
types of equipment. It is likely that new high speed, high density
ECL processes will be introduced to meet this need. Many govern-
ments are spending considerable sums of money supporting such
research projects; the U.S. Department of Defense funded Very
High Speed Integrated Circuits (VHSIC) Programme is probably
the most well known of these.

Why ECL? Since digital data rates are at least twice those of the
sampled analogue signal — and most requirements are for signals at
radio frequencies — the choice of technology is limited. But this
data is then analysed, each bit requiring 10 or more multiplications, additions or subtractions, so that the processing rate is
already at the limit of today's ECL capabilities.

A popular example of digital signal processing is the application
of the Discrete Fourier Transform (DFT) to convert a set of signal
amplitudes sampled at regular time intervals ($t_0 \ldots t_n$) into a set
of amplitudes of the component frequencies ($f_0 \ldots f_n$). In other
words the DFT decomposes a time function into its frequency
components. The DFT requires many calculations to be performed,
and even at audio frequencies over 100 million multiplications and
additions are needed every second to process real-time data with
reasonable accuracy. For this reason many alternative algorithms
(known collectively as Fast Fourier Transforms or FFTs) have
been developed to eliminate the redundant calculations.

It is worth looking briefly at a simple application of the DFT so that its potential can be realised and the necessary circuitry understood. The transform is as follows.

If N samples are taken at equal time intervals the frequency element k (of a total of N) is

$$f(k) = \sum_{n=0}^{(N-1)} A_n\,(\cos B - \mathrm{j}\sin B)$$

where A_n is the amplitude of the signal at time n and $B = 2\pi nk/N$.

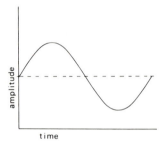

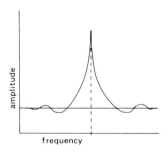

Fig. 8.1 Discrete Fourier Transform

Fig. 8.1 illustrates the result. The frequency spectrum of f in fig. 8.1 is shown as having a finite bandwidth. This is due to the fact that a finite number of samples have been taken; as the number of samples is increased the uncertainty diminishes and eventually f becomes a single line (assuming that the frequency is constant).

There are many applications of the DFT and FFT but one further example will show how useful they can be. Consider the measurement of speed using radar techniques. A transmitter

operating at frequency f_1 bounces the signal off a moving object —
a car or aircraft, for example. The returning signal f_2 is shifted in
frequency due to the Doppler effect — upwards for an approach-
ing object, downwards for departing — and the radar receiver
mixes this with f_1 to obtain the difference frequency $(f_2 - f_1)$. If
the difference frequency is continuously digitised and transformed
from the time to frequency domain a frequency plot will be
available every 1000 samples or so (see fig. 8.2). It is easy to
observe the relative velocity and take corrective action — far more
so than by looking at a conventional radar screen.

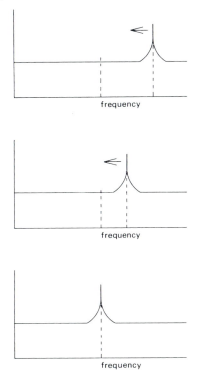

Fig. 8.2 Doppler shift

In practice it is possible to add this type of information to an
otherwise normal display; once information is present in digital
form it becomes much easier to process it further.

Returning to the operation of a DFT, it can be seen that a total
of N^2 complex multiplications ($4N^2$ real multiplications) must be
carried out in order to calculate the complete frequency spectrum.
The FFT requires fewer — approximately $5N$ complex — but is
still demanding. Furthermore, the FFT cannot calculate only a

part of the spectrum. Most of the FFT calculation involves the removal of two complex words from memory, their multiplication and addition and subsequent return to the same memory locations. This operation is known as a 'butterfly' and is the subject of many mathematical publications.

The FFT processor can be constructed using either a 'data arithmetic unit' or a bank of multipliers/accumulators controlled from a sequencer (program memory) together with a read-only memory (ROM) which stores the values of sines and cosines. Fig. 8.3 shows a possible arrangement.

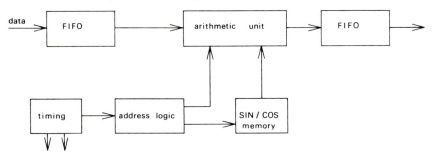

Fig. 8.3 FFT processor

Present day FFT processors use either a large number of separate ICs (not normally ECL) or a smaller number of custom circuits. Since most of the customers today have small volume, high price military applications in mind it is not possible to buy the custom circuits they use. By 1990 digital signal processing will be commonplace and high speed, high density FFT components in ECL technology will be available.

The Fourier transform is one of many algorithms used for processing data. The majority of others require combinations of adders, multipliers, registers and memories together with (in the low level integration solutions of today) a host of high speed 'glue' circuits to interface everything.

Few subsystems for signal processing are yet available in ECL. Although multiplier circuits exist, their complexity is less than those using CML technology and produced by TRW. Typical of their range of multiplier circuits is the TDC1010J, shown in the form of a logic diagram in fig. 8.4. Two 16 bit words can be multiplied in 100 ns, approximately twice as long as in ECL.

While the DFT and FFT are ideal for spectrum analysis and the measurement of frequencies, broadly similar circuit techniques allow the design of digital filters. A simple first-order discrete time filter requires only three circuit blocks — an adder, multiplier and shift register. Fig. 8.5 shows how these are connected.

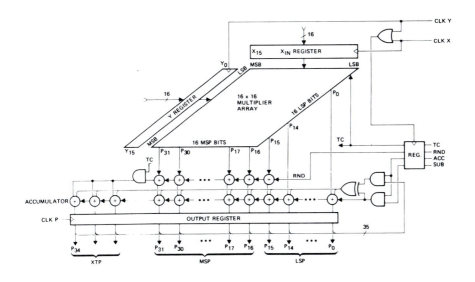

Fig. 8.4 16 by 16 multiplier configuration

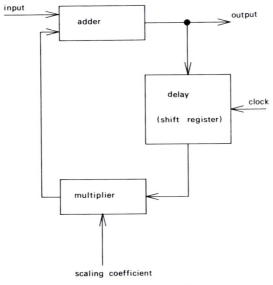

Fig. 8.5 Simple digital filter

The digital output consists of the summation of the input signal and a fraction of the input signal of several cycles ago. The time delay (a shift register, clocked at the data rate) is fixed. To understand how the filter operates consider the case when, at high input frequencies, the delay corresponds to a phase shift of 180 degrees. It is therefore out of phase with the incoming signal and will reduce its amplitude. At lower frequencies the same delay will have only a slight effect on the phase shift and the output will tend to be increased. This then becomes a low pass filter.

A single filter is of limited use and most applications call for ten or more poles at analogue input frequencies of up to 1 MHz. There are two methods of building complex filters and one is shown in fig. 8.6.

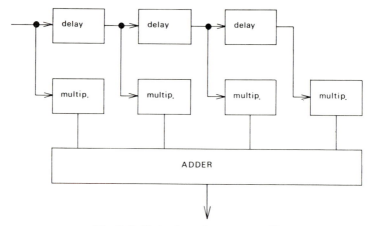

Fig. 8.6 Finite impulse response filter

The FIR filter behaves like a tapped delay line and has the advantage of unconditional stability. No signal feedback is applied and for this reason the filter design is known as 'non-recursive'. The phase response is linear and although many components are required to construct a filter with many poles it is still relatively easy to design and implement.

The second type of filter has an infinite impulse response (IIR) and appears in fig. 8.7. Although the IIR (recursive) filter may require fewer components it can become unstable and is less tolerant of small changes in component values. Its principal advantage lies in the similarity to conventional analogue filters; the feedforward and feedback terms can be mathematically related to zeros and poles (respectively).

The calculation of digital filters is a well documented subject for which several computer programs are available. It is common to analyse the performance of filters in the time (rather than frequency) domain and this involves the use of another algorithm — the Z transform.

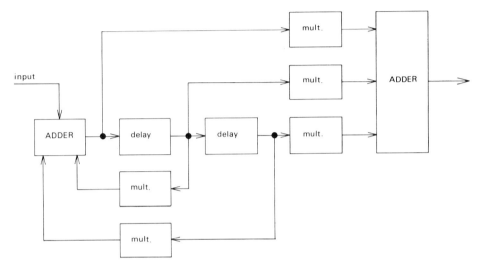

Fig. 8.7 Infinite impulse response filter

Digital 'correlation' is a further example of signal processing, but of a different kind. Although there are few applications at present outside sophisticated radar and transmission systems the recognition of a pattern in digital (or digitised analogue) signals offers immense potential. A correlator normally compares an input signal with a stored pattern (this is known as 'cross-correlation') but an alternative method (known as 'auto-correlation') allows the comparison of an input with a delayed portion of itself so that hidden patterns of frequency can be identified. In either case the correlator can identify the presence of a desired signal even when this is masked by the presence of noise — a boon in communications equipment. A simple form of correlator is shown in fig. 8.8.

The digital input signal is clocked at the data rate through the input shift register. Each bit is continuously compared with the corresponding data bit in the reference shift register (which is not clocked unless configured as an auto-correlator). The comparison takes place in a series of EXCLUSIVE-OR gates which give an output of 1 only when both inputs are at 1. These outputs are summed so that the number of matching bits (the degree of correlation) can be monitored continuously. Subsequent circuitry can take appropriate action — for example, to count the number of clock pulses between output peaks (to measure the pattern repetition frequency) or to alter the contents of the reference if matching is not achieved.

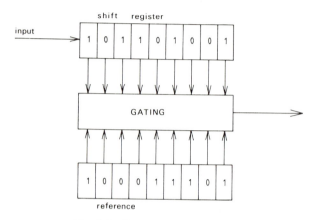

Fig. 8.8 Simple digital correlator

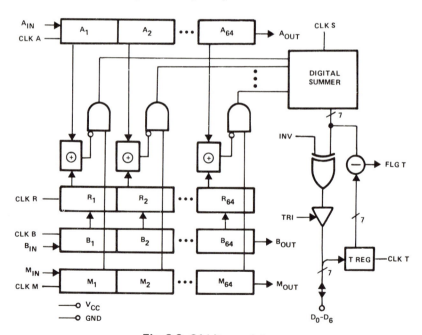

Fig. 8.9 64 bit correlator

Auto-correlation requires the input signal to be fed into the reference register via a variable delay — possibly another shift register. Alternatively the input can be disconnected and fed instead from the end of the input shift register so that the data is 'recirculated'.

Few correlators are available for sale as such. Several custom ECL circuits are in production but TRW have a range of off-the-shelf CML products which operate at data rates of up to 15 MHz. See fig. 8.9 for a block diagram of their 64 bit correlator. The correlator inputs are shown as A and B; M is a masking input to deselect bits which are not to be used for comparison. A threshold register at the output indicates when a specified output level has been reached.

A specific application of correlation is in error detection and correction in systems where data is transmitted in a certain pattern. When an error is detected in the pattern then the contents of the input shift register are altered bit by bit in a predetermined way until the error is cleared. Meanwhile the new input data is stored in a FIFO (first in, first out memory) and the correlation rate subsequently increased until it has been emptied. Although circuits are normally designed for specific types of data error detection a general purpose ECL error correction circuit is available from Motorola. The MC10905 is a 16 bit device but can be expanded to 64 bits if necessary. Error detection takes only 17 ns; correction another 20 ns. Its disadvantage lies only in the inevitable complexity of a 'universal' product; a 68 lead package and a power consumption of 4.5 W.

The principles of error detection apply also to the extraction of synchronising pulses from streams of data. Header codes and special patterns (e.g. for PCM frame sync) can be identified.

Allied to advances in digital signal processing itself are several circuit techniques which improve processing speed and accuracy. The impact of the microprocessor in computing applications has not gone unnoticed! More traditional parallel processing methods are needed to maximise the speed but the resulting loss of flexibility is also a consideration. In a parallel processor many logic decisions can take place simultaneously. In the type of parallel processor used in signal processing the input is normally split into several parts (perhaps one for each bit) and each part is processed at the same time in similar sections of circuitry. Finally the separate parts are recombined at the output. Parallel processing may only be needed in those parts of the circuit where speed is critical. See fig. 8.10.

The concept of parallel processing can also be applied to systems which include a central processor. The algorithm and associated control is dealt with by one group of circuits; the interfacing by another, and so on. This 'federated' type of architecture (in which .each part functions independently up to a certain level) can readily be adapted to cater for fault conditions of the type likely to be encountered in a military environment. However a true parallel processor contains identical sections of circuitry operating in parallel at an overall data rate higher than a single section could achieve.

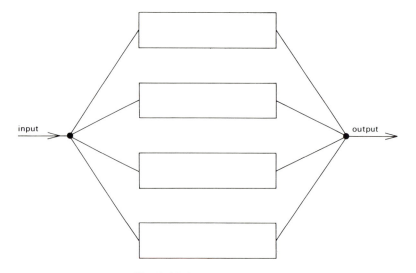

Fig. 8.10 Parallel processing

Another fast processing architecture concept is that of the pipeline. This implies that the algorithm itself is split into several units, each handled by a separate part of the circuitry. Like the parallel processor, at a given time many logic decisions are taking place — but in this case they take place on different data. This is analogous to a factory production line where the product passes along the line, one worker fitting a panel, the next tightening the bolts . . .; the product may take one hour to complete its journey but once the line is full the production *rate* could be one per minute, assuming it takes no longer than one minute to perform a single task. So the data rate of a pipelined processor is high — and is based on the time it takes to perform one part of the algorithm rather than the complete algorithm. See fig. 8.11. A common example of pipelining is in the design of a digital multiplier. Consider the two diagrams of fig. 8.12.

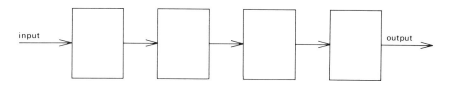

Fig. 8.11 Pipelined processor architecture

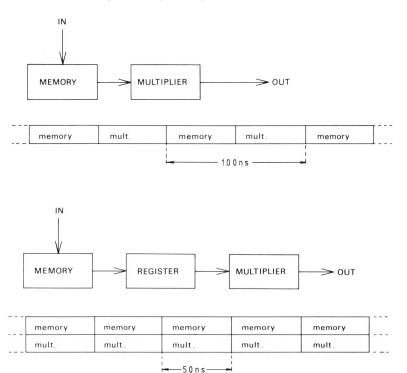

Fig. 8.12 Example of pipelined multiplication

In the conventional multiplier configuration there are two specific operations. The first, which takes 50 ns in this example, is to fetch data from the required memory addresses and store them in the multiplier. Then the data is multiplied and the output fed to a register; this also takes 50 ns. These operations cannot be carried out simultaneously because the data in the multiplier cannot be changed during multiplication. It therefore takes 100 ns to perform the total operation and outputs appears every 100 ns – a data rate of 10 MHz.

The pipelined version includes an extra register which acts as a temporary store for the data fetched from memory for the NEXT multiplication. In other words the multiplier no longer has to wait for the memory to be accessed every time. The delay caused by the extra register is normally not significant so although it still takes 100 ns to perform the total operation the outputs now appear every 50 ns — a data rate of 20 MHz. The disadvantage is a slight increase in complexity and a delay (two clock cycles in this case) to 'fill the pipe'.

The use of pipelined architecture allows data rates to be limited only by the slowest elements of the circuit. By paralleling these elements (if possible) the data rate can be further increased. Reverting for a moment to the example of a production line, if the slowest operation is the fitting of a panel and the operation cannot be subdivided (you cannot fit half!) then using two or three workers for this operation to save time corresponds to the concept of parallel processing. Thus the combination of these two circuit techniques offers major scope for fast digital signal processing.

A concept widely applied to scientific calculators in order to extend their range of numbers is that of 'floating point' arithmetic. A number is divided into two parts, the 'mantissa' (a number from 0.1 to 0.999 . . . with so many decimal places) and the 'exponent' (an integer to indicate the power of 10 by which the mantissa is to be multiplied). Therefore the number

$$0.735 \times 10^8 \ (M = 0.735, E = 8)$$

is the floating point version of

$$73500000.$$

There is no reason why the same concept cannot be adapted for use in signal processing so that the 'dynamic range' (the ratio of largest to smallest) of the signal can be extended. A 10 bit mantissa and 6 bit exponent (16 bits) give a dynamic range of over 10^{20} compared to less than 10^5 for a conventional 16 bit word. The subsequent signal processing — especially addition — is more complex although floating point multiplication is relatively easy; the mantissa parts are multiplied and the exponents added. Addition is not so simple but TRW manufacture a 24 bit FP adder in CML (not ECL) which adds two numbers, each with 16 bit mantissa and 6 bit exponent, in only 100 ns. It is known as the TDC1022 and a block diagram appears in fig. 8.13.

The methods of signal processing outlined so far only represent a sample of the variety of circuit techniques and algorithms currently being used. Within a decade most of the subsystems will be available as individual ICs but today the applications are aimed at (and funded by) specific military projects – radar, sonar, imaging, surveillance and secure communications. The principal applications outside these areas are as follows:

Spectrum analysis
Noise reduction
Broadcast TV
Digital modems
Image recognition
Instrumentation
Navigation
Radio communication

Most of these rely heavily on analogue circuitry at present; the introduction of new ECL products within the next few years promises to make sweeping changes.

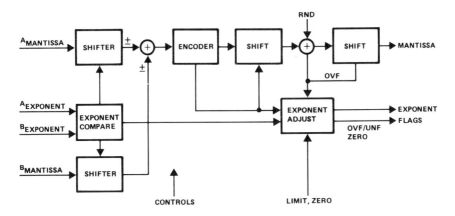

Fig. 8.13 TRW floating point adder

Applications in secure communications are representative of what can be done with the products available now. Using 'spread spectrum' techniques in which the transmitted signal bandwidth occupies only a few percent of the total available bandwidth at a given time it is possible to conceal the signal beneath the noise level corresponding to that bandwidth. This can be done by modulating the signal on to a low level carrier which has a frequency change every few milliseconds according to a pseudo-random code. This code is held in a ROM and used either to drive a frequency synthesiser, or, in the case of pulse modulation at frequencies below 100 MHz, possibly even a DAC (the effect is sometimes known as 'frequency hopping' although this term can be applied to other arrangements). Extracting the signal is a difficult enough task for the receiver which has the code in ROM — but virtually impossible (in real time, anyway) for anyone else. Unless the precise bandwidth at a given time is known it should not be easy even to detect that the transmitter is operating — a point of great interest to those who need to conceal the transmitter location. Although many transmitters can occupy the same range of frequencies there is a finite risk of interference which, in practice, limits the maximum number of channels to rather fewer than normal with conventional frequency allocation. Although this limitation and the overall complexity rule out the majority of non-military uses there is no reason why this should not change. After all, fast-hopping synthesisers are now being seriously proposed for low cost cellular radiotelephone systems. Considerable size and weight advantages could accrue if the transmitted output power of the portable equipments were to be reduced. Extra complexity at the base station would add little to overall costs.

Now that some applications of digital signal processing have been described it is worth while looking at the ECL products available. The biggest problem is that most of the research and development is leading to the production of custom and semi-custom ICs which will never be available on the open market. TRW manufacture a wide range of LSI circuits in CML; AMD and many others produce Schottky TTL parts but neither has the speed of ECL. Both Motorola and Plessey offer a few dedicated products and there are many other standard parts which are suitable. Here is a summary of those most likely to be useful.

The simplest of these is the fast ECL gate; there are high speed versions of both ECL3 and 10K products. Table 8.1 is a comparison of standard and high speed versions of each:

Table 8.1

ECL3	1660	16F60 (Plessey)
Max. prop delay	1.6 ns	0.8 ns
Max. risetime	2.1 ns	0.6 ns
Max. supply current	28 mA	28 mA
ECL10K	10101	10H101 (Motorola)
Max. prop delay	2.9 ns	1.5 ns
Max. risetime	3.3 ns	2.0 ns
Max. supply current	26 mA	26 mA

Fig. 8.14 compares the switching times of 10K and Motorola 10KH.

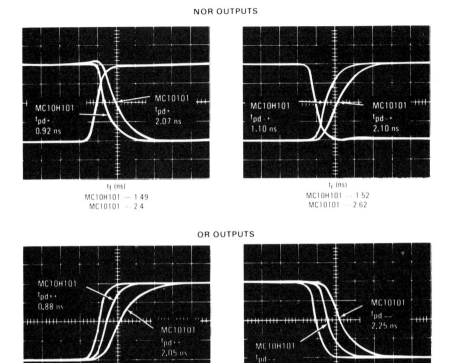

Fig. 8.14 Switching time comparison — 10K, 10KH

Similar higher speed versions of flip-flops are also available; the three shown in table 8.2 all have similar pinning and are dual-D types:

Table 8.2

	ECL10K 10131	ECL10K 10231	ECL10KH 10H131	Plessey SP9131
Max. setup time (ns)	2.5	1.0	1.5	1
Max. toggle frequency (MHz)	125	200	250	520
Max. supply current (mA)	56	65	56	87

There is a clear tradeoff between supply current and frequency (and price!).

Several other selections, variations and improvements of ECL logic products are produced by Fairchild and Motorola. ECL100K could also be considered but interfacing requires special attention.

Moving towards a higher level of integration, latches and shift registers have important parts to play in the correct timing of data inputs and outputs. Apart from the normal ECL10K quad latches (10133, 10153 and 10168) there is a faster quint latch (10175). As yet there are no 10KH versions although Plessey offer a dual 4 bit latch (SP9210) intended for retiming 8 bit bus lines — for example, after parallel-series data conversion. Brief specifications are as follows:

	10175	SP9210
Number of bits	5	8
Max. clock delay	4.3 ns	3 ns
Max. setup time	2.5 ns	1.5 ns
Max. supply current	97 mA	180 mA

Fast shift registers are widely used for temporary storage of serial data when incoming and outgoing rates vary for a short time (when error correction is taking place, for example). The problem is that hardly any of them appear to be available for general sale. There is a 10KH version of the popular 10141 and it promises a minimum rate of 250 MHz. This is a relatively complex product, allowing shifts in both directions and serial/parallel interchanges without external gating (see fig. 8.15).

More complex ICs such as adders and multipliers are also hard to find. Standard ECL10K offers only a dual 2 bit adder (10180) although Plessey offer an 8 bit latched adder, the SP9218. This is shown in fig. 8.16.

Apart from the 10183 4 x 2 multiplier (which is expandable but takes eight packages and typically 43 ns to multiply two 8 bit numbers) Motorola has recently announced the MC10901, an 8 x 8 product taking only 24 ns (max). This is much faster but still not as complex as the TRW 16 bit device. The MC10901 is based on the Motorola semicustom 'Macrocell Array' but is sold as a standard product. The logic diagram appears in fig. 8.17.

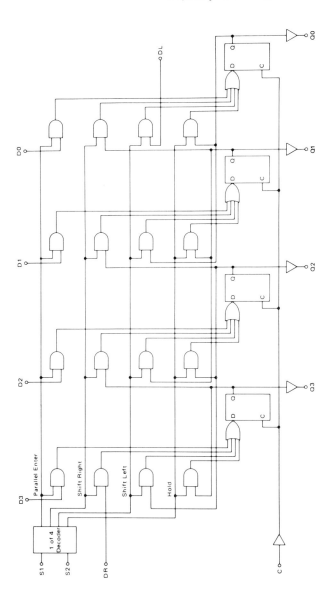

TRUTH TABLE

SELECT		OPERATING MODE	OUTPUTS			
S1	S2		$Q0_{n+1}$	$Q1_{n+1}$	$Q2_{n+1}$	$Q3_{n+1}$
L	L	Parallel Entry	D0	D1	D2	D3
L	H	Shift Right*	$Q1_n$	$Q2_n$	$Q3_n$	DR
H	L	Shift Left*	DL	$Q0_n$	$Q1_n$	$Q2_n$
H	H	Stop Shift	$Q0_n$	$Q1_n$	$Q2_n$	$Q3_n$

*Outputs as exist after pulse appears at "C" input with input conditions as shown. (Pulse = Positive transition of clock input).

Fig. 8.15 10H141 shift register

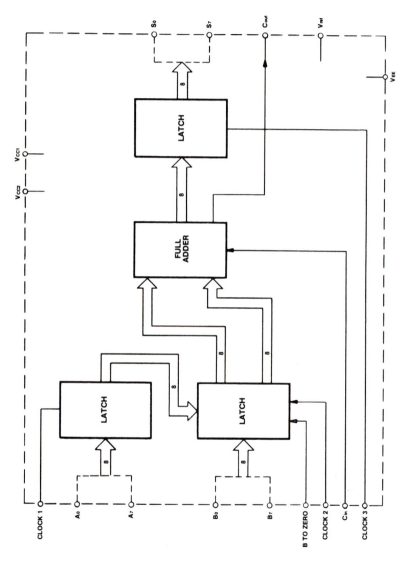

Fig. 8.16 SP9218 latched adder

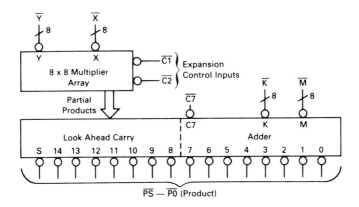

Fig. 8.17 MC10901 multiplier

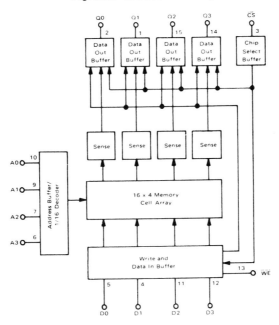

Fig. 8.18 10145 64 bit register

Memories and registers have a large part to play in signal processing systems. Both read/write (RAM) and read only (ROM) memories are required and fortunately both are available in 10K. For small registers the 10145 is useful; the new 10H145 offers a twofold improvement in address access time to 7.5 ns maximum. The circuit configuration is 16 x 4 bits and is shown in fig. 8.18.

Larger RAMs include the 10146 (1024 x 1 bit) which is available with access times down to 10 ns. The larger 4096 bit products are not quite as fast.

High speed ROMs seem more difficult to obtain despite the fact that they are used widely for sine and cosine generation in FFT processors. A 256 x 4 bit PROM such as the 10149 has access times of 25 ns compared with 10 ns or less for a (custom) ROM.

A more advanced approach to digital signal processing involves the use of the ALU (arithmetic logic unit), the heart of a conventional microprocessor but fabricated in ECL. There is nothing new about the ALU concept; they have been available for 10 years in TTL and originated in the form of a programmable gate. The ALU is an interconnected network of gates, shift registers, adders etc. with a group of inputs and corresponding outputs. A second group of inputs control the functions performed by the network; one input may determine whether or not the shift register is bypassed, another if the outputs are to be inverted, and so on. The overall effect is that a single ALU can take the place of any one of a number of different circuits according to the way it has been programmed. More important, its function can be changed by changing a few logic levels. This is still a long way from the microprocessor, although by connecting inputs and outputs to the same RAM the data can be reprocessed as required.

Motorola offer a choice of three types of ALU. The MC10800 is a 4 bit expandable system with a wide range of peripheral circuits including a microprogrammer and memory interface. Details of this series appear in the ECL10K chapter. The MC10900 and MC10902 are both 8 bit 'slices' (i.e. expandable); the first offers the added feature of a ninth 'parity check' bit, the second offers the ability instead to operate on both binary and BCD data. Both are packaged in a 68 pin leadless chip carrier package (like a flat-pack without the leads) and require special cooling arrangements to cope with nearly 4.5 W of power dissipation! Fig. 8.19 shows a block diagram of the MC10900.

Despite the complexity of this diagram the flow of data can be seen. Inputs come from both X bus and Y bus (at the top) and are latched before being routed to the logic networks and eventually to the Z output bus. There are various carry and overflow inputs and outputs. The X, Y and Z bus lines each have 9 bits — the extra bit being a parity check; there are subsequent checks throughout the system to check for errors.

The following operations are performed by the MC10900:

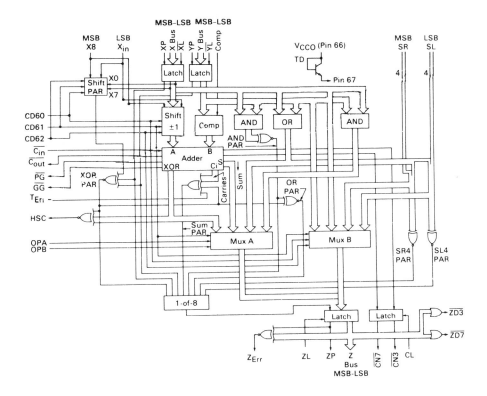

Fig. 8.19 Motorola MC10900

X plus Y (plus carry in),
X plus −Y (plus carry in),
X EXOR Y,
X EXOR −Y,

the above 4 operations with X shifted left or right by 1 bit,

X AND Y,
X OR Y,
  X,
  Y,
X OR Y shifted left or right by 4 bits.

It takes a maximum of 18 ns to add X plus Y. The MC10900 is a relatively complex circuit and reference should be made to the data for more information.

The MC10902 has rather a different configuration. Input data comes from one of three input bus lines A, B and C – outputs go to a single Y bus. See fig. 8.20.

A total of 34 operations can be performed on the input data, the speed being similar to that of the MC10900. It is possible that the complexity of these two products may limit their usefulness in some of the applications described already, but the flexibility of their approach offers exciting possibilities.

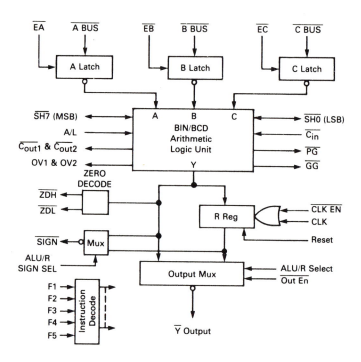

Fig. 8.20 MC10902

The ALU represents one of several possible approaches to the high level integration of digital processors. Apart from a specific design (using semicustom ECL arrays, perhaps) there are several combinations of multipliers, accumulators, adders and gates which can form a relatively small 'cell'. An IC containing a large number of such cells interconnected in a certain pattern may still have the flexibility to allow medium volume production, while still offering outstanding performance. Without doubt there will be many new products in this area during the next decade!

CHAPTER 9
Semicustom ECL

Integrated circuits can only be produced economically in relatively large volumes. The cost of design and manufacture must include the following costs which are almost independent of the volume manufactured:

Design
Layout
Digitisation and mask manufacture
Product engineering
Test engineering
Applications and data production
Marketing and product launch costs

Obviously some of these costs increase when large volume production is envisaged. The cost of a test package, for example, can vary from that to produce a simple test box to a fully automated system. But in practice it costs a lot of money to design, develop and introduce any new product. It makes sense, therefore, to attempt to manufacture ranges of similar products – a logic family, for example – where at least some of the costs can be shared over a number of products. In the ECL10K range several simple gate designs are produced from a single set of masks by changing just one or two masks. The test systems accommodate all variants and many of the other costs are shared also.

When a customer asks a manufacturer to design, develop and produce a custom circuit uniquely for himself he normally has to fund at least 50% of the costs (and undertake to buy enough products to pay for the rest) before the project can even be considered. ECL 'custom designs' tend to be very expensive because of the higher risk factor (of a design proving difficult or impracticable) and the generally higher costs throughout. For the same reason 'customer designs' (where the customer is responsible for design and layout in accordance with the manufacturer's 'design rules' for that process) are not often advised, especially for complex or difficult projects. This is a pity for several reasons.

The speed of an ECL system is governed largely by its physical layout. Lots of packages, especially with transmission line interconnections, waste as much as 1 ns per pin in the logic path. By combining several packages into one then all this speed can be saved.

The power consumption of an ECL system is similarly determined partly by package interconnections. Every time a logic output pin is included it has to drive a 50 Ω (or 100 Ω) line. This adds several milliamps to the power requirement – the exact figure depending on the load resistor chosen – but internal connections require only microamps because of the short length.

The overall size of an ECL system depends on both packing density and power consumption. Custom ECL wins on both counts, often saving the cost of special cooling arrangements as well.

The advantages of custom ECL, at least in a system which requires twenty packaged devices or more, are enormous. Some products, of course, are best left out of any custom circuit – memories, for example, cannot always be included. But IC manufacturers are under considerable pressure to lower the cost of custom circuits.

Their solution is to offer a small range of 'semicustom' ECL logic products. A typical semicustom circuit is made up of several identical 'cells' together with some interface circuitry. The actual chip size is fixed, as is the layout and all masks except those (normally one or two) which determine how the elements within each cell – and all the cells – are connected together. The customer has freedom only to choose the connection pattern he wants – and then only within the rules supplied.

The semicustom approach in this cell-based layout form does save cost appreciably. This is helped by (the almost essential) computer automation of the whole semicustom design process. The best way to understand this is to look at a typical example. Fig. 9.1 illustrates a typical cell design.

This particular cell is based on a two input OR/NOR gate but can be 'wired up', together with components in adjacent cells, to produce flip-flops, counters, and almost anything else available in the 10K range. The design also offers the possibility of using non-standard ECL levels within the chip to reduce power consumption and increase speed. Power supplies are available throughout the chip and one −1.29 V bias generator is provided within every group of four cells. Fig. 9.2 illustrates a very simple design example.

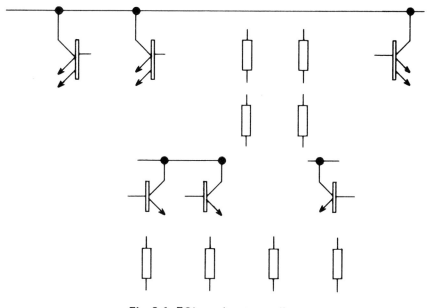

Fig. 9.1 ECL semicustom cell

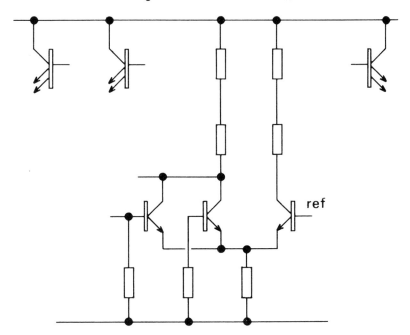

Fig. 9.2 ECL gate array design

The cell design shown is produced in two sizes — 36 cells and 144 cells — each with associated input, output and power supply circuitry. The smaller chip has provision for up to 28 pin connections; the larger up to 64. The customer chooses which chip size is suitable and aims to use 70 or 80% of the available cell components for an optimum design.

This 'gate array', 'uncommitted logic array', 'cell-based array' or similar type of semicustom IC built up from identical cells is the only type of semicustom ECL system widely available today. In the future it is possible that different types of cell will be offered on each chip, leading ultimately to a cell-based *design* where only those cells required (chosen from a library of cells offering functions such as D type flip-flops etc.) would be placed on the chip. The chip size would then no longer be fixed, leading to lower costs (in exchange for a longer development time).

Cell array *(identical cells)*	*Cell design* *(each chosen from a library)*
Fixed chip size	Variable chip size
Short development	Longer development
Medium development cost	High development cost
Medium unit cost	Lower unit cost

If you want to design a semicustom ECL IC then the first problem is to choose a manufacturer. Fig. 9.3 gives the names and capabilities of the major manufacturers. For the first design it is often easier to use the facilities and expertise of a local design house (if there is one). In any case it is important to obtain the latest information before taking decisions.

Having selected a manufacturer and finalised the commercial details the design must then be made. Perhaps a working design exists already. In that case it may be necessary to check the design again to allow for differences in propagation delay, edge speeds and internal logic configuration between the prototype and the semicustom version. The manufacturer should have a logic simulation program to allow this to be done.

If a working design has never been produced it should not take much longer to generate and simulate something which is satisfactory. The time taken to do this depends largely on the experience of the designer in using the program — first designs are the most difficult.

Fig. 9.3 Semicustom ECL manufacturers

Fairchild (GE1000) up to 2000 gates. Propagation delays down to 0.5 ns.

Hitachi up to 1500 gates. Propagation delays down to 0.35 ns.

Motorola (MCA series) up to 2500 gates, some arrays with RAM or registers on-chip. Propagation delays down to 0.5 ns.

National have a second-source agreement with Motorola.

Philips (RTC, Signetics, Mullard) (ACE range) up to 2200 gates, either 10K or 100K compatible. Some arrays contain RAM and propagation delays are down to 0.35 ns.

Plessey (SCD range) up to 300 gates. Propagation delays down to 0.55 ns.

Siemens up to 1000 gates. Propagation delays down to 0.5 ns.

Many more semicustom ECL arrays are in production but not generally available; others are being introduced soon.

The next stage involves the agreement of a final test specification for the product. A test program will be generated automatically (assuming a suitable program exists) but certain tests are more critical than others and must be specified. Voltage ratings and operating temperature ranges must also be agreed.

Once all this has been done the circuit design must be translated into a form suitable for implementation on the logic array. The interconnections on the array must then be decided and the circuit operation simulated once again. This whole operation consists of a long sequence of 'try and see' tasks which make it ideal for computerisation. It may look simple enough to sit down with pencil and paper to determine the connections, but utilising, say, 75% of all the components in the array with only two levels of connections is far from easy. Even if successful, the length of the interconnections will affect the performance and involve several attempts to 'juggle' parts of the layout. And then it still has to be checked! Computer-aided design makes this so much easier.

At the end of this 'layout' stage the final simulation must be agreed. At this point the test program can be prepared while masks (normally a set of three) are being manufactured. Partly processed slices (wafers) of the cell array are normally held in stock by the manufacturer and it is relatively simple to complete processing using the new masks.

Finally the finished wafers can be probe tested (while still in wafer form) using a simplified form of the test program. This test eliminates the majority of non-functional chips before assembly and helps to reduce costs. After the wafers are separated into individual chips (dice) they are inspected, assembled and tested.

The costs and timescales for semicustom design and development are both less than half those for a full custom design. Unit costs may be greater, especially when high quantities are envisaged, but the same manufacturer may be prepared to produce a custom ECL design in exchange for a large order (the cost saving being used to pay for the design).

So semicustom ECL offers a major opportunity for the medium to large user of ECL to take advantage of what the process can offer — and hopefully to save money as well.

CHAPTER 10
The future

Major advances in MOS processing technology during the last five years have brought the 'microchip invasion' into everyday conversation. Telephone systems have been revolutionised. Home computers, unheard of ten years ago, can be purchased for less than the cost of a TV set. But MOS, although high in packing density, remains fundamentally a low speed process. The major driving force behind the advance has been the need to reduce the size — and hence the cost — of complex chips. Reductions in size have led to speed improvements.

The method used to optimise yield for a given chip size and to point the way to further improvements is rather complicated, but almost predictable in results. A particular set of masks using, say, 5 micron geometries is reduced in size, perhaps to 4 microns. A comparison is made between the yields obtained from the two sets of masks — the reduced chip size obviously provides a far greater number of chips per slice but of lower yield. It is therefore possible to calculate the 'shrink' necessary to optimise the number of good chips per wafer, and this size of mask used for production purposes.

But this is not all. An analysis of the failed chips from both batches is carried out. In most cases it will be found that a particular design structure within the circuit is responsible for the majority of failures. The reason for this is then analysed and an attempt made (often using a 'test mask' containing a variety of possible implementations of this part of the circuit) to correct this. If the pattern cannot be reduced in size, perhaps a small increase in size may be permissible provided there is no significant increase in the overall chip size. Then the whole exercise is repeated once more.

Eventually a point is reached where no further design improvements can be made. At this point an attempt is made to optimise those parts of the process which limit yields. The type of mask alignment, doping levels and temperatures, metallisation techniques — all these are carefully studied (using test structures of course) until those improvements have been maximised. Then it is back to the design again . . .

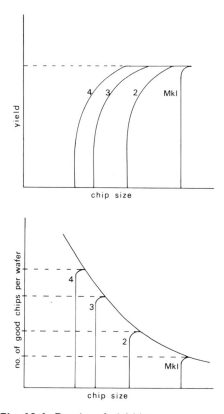

Fig. 10.1 Results of yield improvements

This determined, perhaps even frantic, effort to reduce the cost of complex integrated circuits has had remarkable results. The diagrams of fig. 10.1 illustrate what can be achieved.

Although MOS technology has been able to take advantage of this cost-cutting approach, it is possible to improve bipolar processes in exactly the same way. Most experts agree that within eight years a sixteenfold improvement in circuit complexity will be obtained (by reduction of geometries from 4 to 5 microns down to 1 micron). Although a non-saturating logic design will be needed to take advantage of the speed improvements that these size reductions will bring, it is not yet clear which techniques will be most suitable and what improvement can be obtained. It is likely, though, that gate propagation delays of less than 400 ps will be achievable with complexities of 10 000 gates per chip with a dissipation of less than 4 W.

The limitation of transistor geometries to 1 micron is based on the use of ultraviolet light and conventional masks. A technology change will be needed to make significant improvements in this – the use of X-rays and of electron beams are being studied at present. Within the eight year period this limitation should be relaxed and further increases in complexity will follow.

The processing methods are also being examined carefully. Conventional high speed bipolar processes are of the type shown in fig. 10.2.

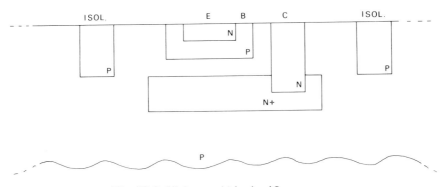

Fig. 10.2 High speed bipolar IC process

Many proprietary process techniques are used to optimise performance, but there are several specific areas of interest:

Ion implantation is widely used to drive controlled levels of impurities into the wafers. Older high temperature gaseous techniques are not sufficiently accurate for small geometries.

Reductions in parasitic resistance are needed to increase transition frequency. A conventional 'buried N' layer (combined with a 'collector sink' diffusion) is adequate for the collector, but improvements in contact resistance and metallisation methods are being sought. Polysilicon emitters, 'flat' emitters and other process modifications are being introduced.

Improved isolation is necessary to reduce interaction between adjacent transistors. Oxide isolation is one of a number of techniques (see fig. 10.3) but other methods allow the use of polysilicon, silicon nitride, or even an empty space to provide the separation. Phrases such as 'dielectric isolation', 'silicon-on-sapphire', 'U-groove structure' and others illustrate the variety of possibilities.

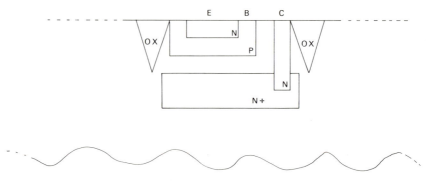

Fig. 10.3 Oxide isolated IC process

Multilayer metallisation is necessary to ease design difficulties and reduce chip size even more. Conventional technology (as for ECL10K) relies on oxide as an insulator, but the uneven surface and risk of cracking have encouraged the use of other materials such as polyimide (a high temperature plastic). Fig. 10.4 illustrates this.

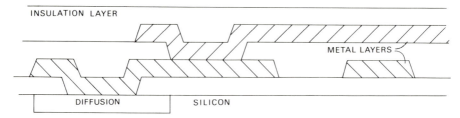

Fig. 10.4 Multilayer metallisation

It is possible that alternative semiconductor materials — gallium arsenide, for example — will replace silicon in some applications. Time will tell.

Allied to all these process improvements are several design novelties. Conventional ECL is rather wasteful of supply voltage in that a power supply of −5.2 V is being used for a circuit with voltage swings of only 700 mV. By re-tolerancing the basic gate design the supply voltage can be reduced to, say, 2.6 V with no change in current consumption (except for the output stage — but this is not important in the case of a complex design). The power consumption is halved immediately. Since 2.6 V supplies are not readily available there are two possibilities:

(a) Separate the 5.2 V supply into two parts so that the 'current is used twice'. Input and output stages may use the full voltage, the first part of the logic the lower supply and, after level shifting, the rest of the logic can use the other supply.
(b) Without creating a specific separation of supplies, arrange the logic in a 'stacked' or 'tree' configuration so that logic decisions can be passed from the lower part to the higher throughout the circuit. This technique is sometimes termed CML (current mode logic) although strictly speaking all ECL is CML anyway.

These techniques are used fairly widely already and are sometimes combined with I^2L (integrated injection logic) which also requires a low voltage supply. See fig. 10.5.

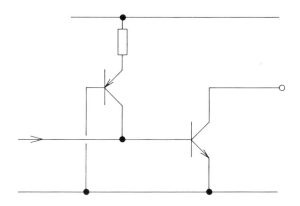

Fig. 10.5 Integrated injection logic

Other 'design mixtures' include Schottky TTL and ECL (the Am29116 from AMD, for example, and many 'TTL' memories) and ISL (Schottky I^2L) with ECL.

If low voltage supplies ever become popular there are some alternative ECL design approaches. Fig. 10.6 illustrates a type of logic known as LDL (linear differential logic) used by AMD for an ADC design. LDL is similar to ECL except for the closely controlled supply voltage of 1.2 V, giving a logic level swing of 130 mV or so.

The fundamental difference between ECL and LDL is the replacement of the voltage reference (which determines the 0 to

1 transition voltage) by a positive feedback connection which has the effect of moving the reference voltage according to the logic state. This renders the design unsuitable for use as a logic family ·because of the exaggerated dependence on supply voltage, transistor matching etc. but ideal for use within an IC. LDL is only one of several possible new versions of ECL design for low voltages but demonstrates the type of development which is taking place.

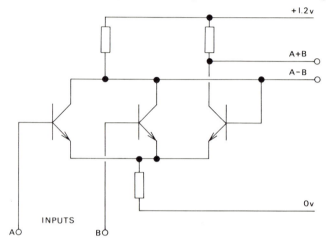

Fig. 10.6 Linear differential logic

Packaging is another area of great interest. Now that more complex circuits are being developed it is essential to find a low cost package suitable for high speed applications but with 40 or more pin connections. The conventional dual-in-line package is rather large and suffers from the unequal internal lead lengths between chip and pins; pins at extreme ends of the package are particularly affected by stray inductance and capacitance which affects circuit operation. A better package is the 'leadless chip carrier' (LCC) shown in fig. 10.7.

Many versions of this package have been proposed and some are already in volume production. Within the basic outline there are hermetic and low cost ceramic packages together with a plastic version with leads bent under the package. These three have identical 'footprints' and can be soldered directly on to printed circuit boards (for smaller package sizes) or mounted on a ceramic substrate.

Other packages tend to have been derived from this outline. 'Pin-grid' packages, for example, can consist of one or more chip carriers mounted on a substrate which has vertical pins suitable for insertion into a socket or a PC board. Simpler pin-grid packages are available, of course.

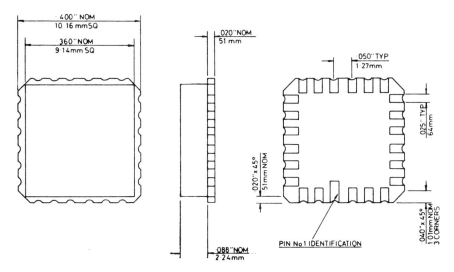

Fig. 10.7 Leadless chip carrier package

Naked chips offer some technical advantages but the difficulty of testing them adequately is a limitation. 'Bump-chips' and 'flip-chips' have never proved successful but 'tape automated bonding' (TAB) is used on a limited scale.

Process improvements, design improvements and the introduction of suitable packages offer the ECL designer a tremendous potential. Faced with enormous increases in speed and complexity he can now design high speed and highly complex circuits never envisaged before. The difficulty is largely in knowing what to design!

The success of logic families such as TTL (and of MOS memories or microprocessors) derived from the assumption that a large and previously untapped market could be found. It is not quite as easy to identify a similar need for the ECL of tomorrow. Much of the research funding today stems from national defence budgets, some of the rest from computer manufacturers. Neither is likely to represent a high volume market, but both are primarily interested in the development of complex signal processors. It follows that this is one area where at least some commercial products will be developed. Data conversion will benefit as a result of this, and a whole new generation of digital radio and TV products could appear.

Further guesses are a little premature, but it is interesting to observe the increasing interest in ECL within the semiconductor industry. Perhaps ECL will never produce a revolution comparable with the 'micro', but it is a far cry from the 'forgotten' high current specialised technology of a decade ago.

Index